Off the Pa

An Anthology of 21st Century American Indian and Indigenous writers, Vol. II

Edited by Adrian L. Jawort

Printed in the United States of America

Published by:
Off the Pass Press LLC
2224 U.S. Highway 87 East #43
Billings, Mont. 59101
www.offthepasspressllc.com

Edited by Adrian L. Jawort

ISBN-13: 978-0986381003

ISBN-10: 0986381004

Cover photo by Tex Jawort

"I stood there in the shadowed doorway thinking with my tears. Yes, tears can be thoughts, why not?"

~Louise Erdich, *The Round House*

Foreword

And so a certain editor/writer was like, "it's cool that you're doing this and all, but you need to get 'f@#k that Sterling' in there." (He actually told me that twice in regards to our mutual friend.) And I'm like, "Well. That's something to say right there. I could never..." and then I thought about it, and you know what? I'm still waiting for his contribution as of now, so that I can write this fully, so: F@#k that Sterling.

Finally, I sat down to write a foreword, a note, a moment "for words," a time to push ahead, to work with this fine collection regardless. And then I get this note last night, "Oh, hey. Sterling's piece is kinda ready. Want to have a look?"

"Yeah. Sure," I say. I get the note over my phone, and I go to open the doc, the attachment, looking forward to this, and, yeah. It won't open.

F@#k that Sterling.

Back to the work at hand. How then to foreword (or, better, forewarn) this book.

How to rise to the task of describing and telling about this book, this collection of such visceral talent?

Of course I wind up starting it by quoting a question someone asked Sterling. "Why are you telling this? It's so dark," they wanted to know.

"Everyone's always telling artists what to do," he says. "And writers write about the things that haunt them." That question and those quotes come from a piece done by Chérie Newman last November for "The Write Question" program on Montana Public Radio. It was called "Beyond Sherman Alexie," and it was an interview with Montana Native writers Adrian Jawort, Luella Brien, Eric Leland BigMan Brien, and Sterling HolyWhiteMountain. In it, the authors were asked about their work and the ambitiously named *Off the Path: An Anthology of 21st*

Century Montana American Indian Writers, Vol. I. They had plenty to say, and gave every indication that there would be more to follow, and after that, there'd be some more. We've got stories, people. Newman says to Jawort: "Adrian, this book's title includes the words 'volume one.' So what's coming next?" "Volume two is coming next (laughs). Volume two I wanted to expand out. We have; farther than I even imagined." It's gone global, for sure. *Volume II* reaches out from Montana, down into the southwest, over to *He Sapa* ('cause heyz, #lakotaway couldn't let that just slide by) and out over the Pacific through Hawai'i, Aotearoa/NZ and into Australia.

In that half-hour program, the authors themselves gave outstanding insights into why you're holding this book right now. Luella Brien talked about her work with students at Little Big Horn College—"I block out my name and have my students read the story... they can't believe this story could live in my head." I think she's talking about something key to know here—this story lives in her head. To be sure, the experiences are described in ways that made her students say "When did this happen? I don't remember this," because yes, there are those experiences on the reservations, in the cities, and in the suburbs, in short, wherever Indians live, but the point is that it's a story well-told by an excellent storyteller, an excellent *writer*. That gets overlooked far too often, like Chief Dan George getting passed over for an Oscar® for *Little Big Man* because Academy voters just thought he was "playing himself, just playing an Indian." These are contemporary writers with plenty to say about us all.

We go back to Sterling (cause f...never mind) and his questioner: "Why are you telling this?" Too often (and here I'm thinking of some films that were refused screenings at certain festivals due to content and other "concerns") Native artists are told what to do, what to show, what to say. It reminds me of the issues experienced by African American intellectuals and artists related to concepts of "racial uplift" beginning in the early twentieth century. Here we are, a hundred years or more later, and, well, here we are.

Let's turn to Eric Leland Bigman Brien, who says, "it's about contemporary Native American life, but it's human. We all can relate to it. These are issues that *everybody* has to deal with. And so it's a good place to start." Adrian adds, "someone told me, they said, 'you captured the hopelessness of wanting to do something,' and that's why they kind of have to just take matters into their own hands." That's what's happening here, folks. For a second volume. Writing for themselves, writing for each other. Possibly they're writing for you. I wouldn't count on it, but that's ok. When you step into these stories you just might find a place in them for you.

Luella Brien talking about Toni Morrison's *The Bluest Eye* described much of the writing collected in the first volume of *Off the Path* as "tragic, but hopeful." Sterling commented, "Indigenous people are always in the way...the desires of nations are for resources and land and there just happens to be a group of people here that are in the way of that desire. That's one of the defining experiences of being indigenous. And so, I think what the anthology does, it will both show some of the universals in terms of experience between indigenous peoples, but also just how different experiences are in the lives that indigenous people are living can really be."

Contributor Cinnamon Spear, in an interview with Indian Country Today Media Network from November as well, said, "There's too much shame...I grew up with alcoholism and abuse, but it doesn't define me, and I'm better for it. We need to tell our kids that they can be strong and brilliant; they just need the tools. Adults too. There's a lot of pain. We have to look each other dead in the eye and tell the truth. We have to listen to our inner voice, and share our stories."

In the MPR interview, Sterling expressed his concern that there are two Crows, a Blackfeet, and a Northern Cheyenne all in the same room.

"Maybe someone won't get out alive," he says. Jokes. Laughs. Hahaha.

Maybe. But if you were ever going to survive all this, all that, you'll need to read this book.

When I first moved to Montana, I met writers. I still meet writers. One day, though, I met these writers all together, at the Roxy Theater in Missoula. I was able to listen to, and watch, the crowd and their reaction to those works from the first volume being read aloud. The reaction was immediate. They knew, and I knew, and I think the writers knew, that something special was happening. That special continues with *Off the Path: Volume II*. I wasn't sure how I would do here as someone from away, someone not Montana Native, or Montana native. But as a Native writer, as a reader, an academic and critic concerned with what we're doing, where we're going, what we've been, and what we can be, that day in the theater? That, like these words, is the real deal.

This goofy, this poignant, this teasing, this pain, this art, this place, this group, these writers, these roads, these scenes, these stories.

This good.

This now.

This home.

This book.

This time,

is theirs.

Theodore C. Van Alst, Jr., Ph.D.
Sihasapa Lakota
Assistant Professor
Native American Studies Department
University of Montana
Missoula, April 2015

Preface

As famed Oglala Lakota Chief Red Cloud once noted it was the Natives' voice that was first heard across this North American land, and therefore the land belonged to them. But as the encroachment of white settlers began to overwhelm his ancestral lands after yet another broken treaty, he told delegates, "Our Nation is melting away like the snow on the side of the hills where the sun is warm, while your people are like the blades of grass in spring, when summer is coming."

Through disease, deception, bloodshed, and starvation by the destruction of primary food sources like the bison, Native groups became isolated, either relegated to small pockets of their former land or forcibly relocated elsewhere. Many tribes resisted, but others were simply eradicated in the cause of the Manifest Destiny state of mind used to justify genocidal behavior.

While the Americans claimed they were "expanding their boundaries of freedom" westward, freedoms for tribal peoples would disappear as even their culture was outlawed. For example, after the Indian Wars effectively ended in the late 19th Century, Native children who dared speak the languages first heard across this land were severely reprimanded and beaten in the boarding schools they were forced to attend far away from their homelands.

"Kill the Indian, save the man," a phrase coined by Richard Henry Pratt of the infamous Carlisle Indian School in Pennsylvania, became a de facto motto for all boarding schools as tribal children were taught to be ashamed of who they were and where came from. "Let all that is Indian within you die!" said Rev. J.A. Lippincott at a Carlisle commencement address. Students were told they could never become "truly American ... until the Indian within you is dead."

But through it all and under the scarred ashes of their collective histories, a fierce, resistant, and proud spirit remained smoldering. Elders told stories that would carry on tribal traditions and history. In fact, storytelling is what kept Natives proud even as Western Civilization attempted to drill into them the notion they were inferior. Storytelling reignited the fire that colonization tried to extinguish.

Then, as more Natives learned to write, we were able to relate on a personal level with other indigenous peoples who we otherwise might not have ever come across. We know we are not alone, and we know we are similar because of the discrimination and hardships we've powered through as a result of our pride and our determination. From South to North America on over to the islands in the Pacific, from Hawaii to New Zealand and Australia, we can now relate to other indigenous people on a base level as stories and struggles are shared.

Yet, despite collective tribulations and even prejudices we've faced, we still recognize and embrace our tribal differences. Our identities are not of a one-size-fits-all pan-indigenous nature, but ones of diverse cultures, languages, and geographical differences. Through those intricate lines we're able to write about our experiences today from uniquely distinct points of view.

And through our experiences and self-expression via the form of written art, we are able to bridge the gap between not only the between indigenous cultures, but also the non-indigenous world. Tourists may witness the beauty of our cultures and lands via powwows, museums, and historical sites. Rarely, however, do they get to know us apart from the stoic caricatures they get from TV, film, or history books. But we are modern people who laugh, love, and feel the pains of our human journey through life. Although we must always remember our ancestors' sacrifices in that we can honor them, our lives are also shaped by current experiences not solely of the distant past.

The *Off the Path* anthologies will allow us breathe out personal stories that may plague our souls via the artistic written word as we aim to intrepidly and genuinely speak right at readers' hearts from our own. In *Volume I*, for instance, my story "He Doesn't Know He's Dead Yet" is about the narrator's brother who was murdered on a cold Montana Indian reservation prairie. That story was based on my own brother's murder, and I described the anguished cries of the bereaved mother while my own mother's real-life cries still echoed in my head.

It might technically be fiction, but many readers definitely know it's real—especially if they've been there too. That's exactly how they felt when their close friend or relative died as the whole world moved on and seemingly didn't care or understand.

The story understood, however, and that's why we write them.

Nea'ese (thank you) for reading our words, and nea'ese to our contributors who have bled out their tears and blood as ink on these pages in order to supply the content to this volume.

~Adrian L. Jawort, Northern Cheyenne

CONTENTS

Small Tremors

By Kenneth Dyer-Redner

You wake from your afternoon nap, sitting upright in the blue chair in the living room. In your cold house, you rise, hug yourself, and rub the goose bumps on your arms as you shiver a bit. You walk to the thermostat and turn it up. You turn to look at the chair and table next to the fireplace, and in your memory you can see your husband of forty-seven years sitting there, resting his elbows on his skinny legs and looking down at his weathered hands. It's too quiet in the house. You think, *Where has he gone? He should be home by now.*

So you walk to your room, take your sweater from the closet, and slide your arms through each sleeve. You walk to the front door, grab your shoes, sit at the table, and slowly tie each of them. You rise from your seat and open the front door. You stare across the landscape, standing on the front steps with the ramp that was built for your husband after his kidneys failed.

You remember that week, years ago, when he came in the house on a hot afternoon. He was acting strange, but you just thought he had been out drinking with his friends. Then you knew something was different, however, when he fell down in the kitchen and looked at you with fear in his eyes and said, "I feel crazy. I don't know. I just feel...crazy." Failed kidneys and diabetes made his blood sugar level dangerously low. So you called your daughter and she drove him to the hospital with you sitting in the backseat praying pleadingly with all of your might.

But now it's just you standing on the front steps as your daughter drives up and parks. You, worrying where your husband has gone; he should be home by now. You, watching your daughter get out of her car and walk up to you, smiling.

"Hey, Momma. Where are you getting ready to go?"

"Over there," you say.

"Over where?"

"Over to your place." You pause, thinking hard, and—"But...I can't find your dad. I don't know where he is. He must be walking around someplace out back, or he probably took off with Ike somewhere."

You feel the cool breeze of autumn, look at your daughter's puzzled face, and also smile.

"What?" you say.

"Mom," she says, "Dad passed away four years ago, remember?"

You stop and think, trying hard to remember. Just then the Earth moves. A small Earthquake. There's been a lot of seismic activity in Northern Nevada lately. You felt the last one a few days ago, lying in bed on a Friday night. It woke you and you grasped the sides of your bed as it shook. After it stopped you went back to sleep.

"Mom," your daughter says, and takes you by the arm, "I said did you eat? You need to eat. Did you take your medication? Here, sit down, I'm gonna make you something to eat."

You sit at the table, in the chair where your husband used to sit. Your daughter hands you a cup of hot tea and toast. You grab the cup, feeling the hot tea warm the mug and your hands. You, watching the steam rise and disappear, trying hard to remember. You sip your tea and your daughter hands you a bowl of leftover chicken soup. She sits opposite of you, taking the medication out of the container labeled *Monday*, and squints her eyes at you.

"Mom," she says, "*Are you okay?*"

"What?" you say and smile. "Yeah." But...what happened?

After you finish eating and take your meds, you sit at the table, listening to the dishes clang against each other as your daughter cleans.

"Mom, do you remember?"

You look at your daughter, standing over the sink and you nod your head, smiling, trying hard to remember what she said.

She shakes her head and you look down at your hands, noticing the wrinkled skin, veins, and sun spots.

"Where's your dad? Have you seen him? I don't know where he went."

Your daughter dries her hands from the dish water, walks toward you, and kneels down to look you in the eyes.

"Mom," she says. "Dad died four years ago." She takes your hand, gently rubbing it. "C'mon, I'll show you."

You look at her hard, seeing your husband's face in hers. Her soft eyes are beginning to tear. She takes you by the arm and leads you outside. You sit in the passenger side and look out the window as she drives across the Indian reservation in Fallon, Nevada. Deserts. Alfalfa fields. Cattle. HUD houses. Indians. Indians. Indians.

She parks and she helps you out of the car. She takes you by the arm. You walk for a little while, and when you stop, she points down at the headstone.

"Mom, this is Dad's grave."

You look down and read the name. You look at the outline of a cowboy roping a cow on the headstone and remember your husband's rough hands and dark skin. You stand in the cemetery looking down at his grave.

"My husband," you say, and begin to cry quietly.

Then the Earth shakes again, and you know it's only a matter of time.

Megapixels and Ringtones
By Adrian L. Jawort

The most ear-piercing sound he'd ever heard was when she turned her head, stared at him briefly with a pitiable look, and said plainly, "I just don't love you anymore."

The noise seemingly left a permanent ringing in Andrew's ear; like a land line telephone dial tone he could never get to stop, and the operator who sounded like an authoritative old lady librarian would not relieve him of the noise and tell him to hang up, dial again, and make another call already. Over and over the words replayed like a steady, maddening hum. He thought it might make him crazy.

Vicki used to say that she loved his weirdness and offbeat sense of humor, but that was replaced by indifferent familiarity and near annoyance at what used to make her genuinely laugh. Love began falling away like frosted leaves and butterflies fluttered carefree no more and became dusty like moths as the cold contempt settled in.

Scientifically speaking, the science of love came down to brain chemistry wiring as the pleasant butterflies created by dopamine excretion wore off and created no more electrical voltage these days. Vicki decided she needed a fresh fix of someone else—anyone—as she deleted their photos together and, with luck, any lingering positive memories that could possibly haunt her future.

Andrew's cell phone made a quick melodic chime as an incoming text arrived. He glanced at it. *Lol* is all the message said.

In contrast, it had been at least four months since she'd told him to leave, yet he still kept her picture as his screensaver. A symbol of years of love it remained to him, as she'd bought him the fancy phone as a birthday present nearly a year earlier. She teasingly held the small box it came in away from him, saying he could have it only if he promised she would be the phone wallpaper pic from then on, or she'd just keep the phone for herself. As soon as it was fully charged she took a selfie shot with lustful shimmering eyes and an affectionate half-smile that silently said, "I love you so."

He happily obliged her deal because the gift gesture meant that much to his own appreciation and love for her. So it didn't seem stalkerish to him that he still kept the promise, only very fool-hearted if not outright depressing. He thought if he ever took her off the screen, she'd be that much more erased from his life. She'd quit him and he knew he'd always be second choice. Every time he glanced at the phone it was a solemn reminder of what she said would never be again—yet somehow the glowing pixels of her face gave him hope.

***

"Six wasted years." That's what she told everyone within earshot right after they broke up. "Six fucking years I waited for him to be someone besides a worthless, inconsiderate drunk."

When she allowed him to see their four-year-old daughter afterward, there were no more looks of lust or even pity, just sneers of disappointment and disgust. Vicki was considering seeking full custody of their baby, and maybe then the child wouldn't be infected by Andrew's introverted persona. It already seemed to make her want to shun people like her dad did as she clung to him tightly around people. She never did that when it was just her and mom. Vicki felt contrite about the passing negative connotations relating to their child, but her mind was a thunder cloud and she was hard-pressed to recall why she found Andrew appealing in the first place.

Vicki wasn't exactly sure what she had wanted Andrew to do with his life. She only knew he was dragging her down physically, emotionally, and now financially. He worked seasonal construction and wrote freelance journalism articles and also stayed awake late at night typing away at whatever fiction it was that never made money. She figured he'd probably always be a starving artist with an unattainable dream of writing full-time. During lulls of construction work they had trouble paying the bills and had even been evicted one winter when their baby was only one. Vicki knew better that no independent woman like herself should ever have to carry a deadweight man.

She admitted Andrew was bright, but thought him a waste of talent since he'd never gotten a college degree or even seriously strived to obtain one by re-registering for school. He just said he owed the school too much money, and there was nothing much he couldn't learn on his own anyway. There were loan forgiveness programs that she pleaded him to look into. With a degree, he could get one of any number of full-time writing-related jobs with a steady check via academia or even a local newspaper. He summarily dismissed all options she presented and it felt like he dismissed not only her opinions, but her dreams as well. She was tired of struggling for nihil, and just wanted to one day own a modest home and stop swimming so hard against the current.

At first she thought it romantically manly he was a carpenter that wrote. She even proudly organized an LLC construction company for him shortly after his mother died. She got a loan to buy tools, and a new truck and everything. Still, she knew he needed to eventually move forward with the intellectual gifts she fell in love with and there were no impending signs he ever would. It was oh so frustrating, akin to banging one's head against the wall trying to get him to get off of his nowhere path so he could succeed.

At least now Vicki knew exactly what she wanted in a man, and that was with the person she'd been flirting with online for weeks before she finally dumped Andrew's loser ass to the curb. She'd dropped that zero to get with a hero, no doubt. She bragged to her close girlfriends about all the new guy was that Andrew wasn't.

College degree? Check. To Vicki, that piece of paper showed commitment to one's education and future, and this *actual* gentleman was thinking about getting a masters, a degree Vicki only needed another year to obtain if only she didn't have to struggle to pay her bills.

Non-oily and light-skinned? Hah! Check. At age 33 Andrew's face looked babyish, but he needed like special oil-free soap just to keep his shine off—it was something they both had joked about, actually. Also, she merely preferred a lighter shade of skin—it wasn't illegal to have aesthetic preferences—and for a half-breed he'd get pretty dark from working outside all summer.

Steady, good paying job and not a freelance writer or construction worker not currently working? Check.

Drinker? Ironically, no check. It was ironic because the primary reason she'd tell people she kicked Andrew out was because of drinking, and her new guy got pretty buzzed up if not drunk nightly. Her snag said he'd lay off of the hard stuff just for her, however. What a sweetheart since he said he enjoyed the fine taste of it so much and only bought high quality scotch and bourbons. He'd satirically describe a taste of wine in-depth with a mock French accent and joke he was a connoisseur—which made Vicki laugh. He always made her laugh. Andrew never made her laugh anymore and at least her new man wasn't a mere lush like Andrew who'd greedily guzzle 10 cheap beers even in the middle of a weekday on a whim.

She knew she was trying to rationalize and justify the irony, but oh well. At the very least her new man wasn't currently an unemployed drunk like Andrew—whom she found passed out on the couch on a fucking Tuesday like a wino after a long workday of her own. She could have punched him in his greasy drunk face as he snored on the couch, clutching a picture of his mother who'd died seven months earlier. Everyone's mom died, but Vicki and her friends were certain he was only using his mom's death as an excuse to drink to excess only lately.

She noticed he didn't even cry when she passed away, and now he wanted to act like he suddenly mourned her instead of going to work?

She didn't mind if a *working man* drank a beer or two after work, but this laying at home all day having a pity party for himself while she worked all day as a college counselor, preaching positive goals and motivation, was just too much for her to handle, particularly during the busiest first days of school. It had sent her over the edge. She'd later joke to her colleagues she should hang Andrew's pic up in her office to demonstrate to her students what happens when you drop out of college—you turn into a loser like that guy. L.O. fucking L!

***

Andrew knew that his drinking was the tipping point for all of his collected disappointments when they broke up. Still, was it doomed from her point of view anyway whether he drank or not? He'd go months without a drink and it never seemed to stop her irritable moods which sometimes lasted for days. He'd be the prime benefactor of shit rolling downhill whether she was mad at her family, work, road rage, or for spoiling their kid too much.

Before, he'd drink heavily several times a week—much to her chagrin—and that was always a peeve of hers, but she tolerated it since he didn't really go out to bars or anything. He sipped alone at night while writing before slamming a bunch while browsing the internet or watching movies before going to sleep. For the most part he seemed functional and unfazed even when he'd drink during daylight hours—although a high tolerance was nothing to boast about.

And yes, for his part early in their relationship Andrew knew and admitted he drank way too much. He cut down in order to save their relationship and had even given up marijuana when they had the baby. For alcoholics there was always a reason to drink—you're sad, mad, or glad—and there's always more reasons not to drink but they did it anyway just because it was conveniently available at every store in

Montana. He readily admitted it was mixture of immaturity and grief that caused him to go overboard at times. He apologized and said he'd do better than being the sloppy drunk passing out on a couch with beer cans piled on the coffee table next to him. Such things had severely tested her endearing love.

Still, Andrew's greatest high would always be making Vicki smile. The heavy drinking days eventually faded as he favored lying next to her instead of said empty beer cans as the buzz and want of alcohol grew stale. Recently, however, want of the latter crept back as she grew icy towards him and Andrew grew tired of always having to tread lightly. It was always a lose-lose situation no matter what he did. Her frigidness combined with his own neglected and barren heart seemed to freeze the very beers themselves when he walked by the store coolers, making them all the more enticing on simmering summer days as he steadily upped his weekly alcohol intake because screw it.

On the morning of Vicki's official first day of the semester–she'd been at the office all the previous week preparing–he decided to quit writing his article because he wanted to drink a beer or few as they seemed a better option than pain pills he loathed that made him sleep forever. He also hated pills for personal reasons after witnessing what they'd done to his mom and even some family friends. His head throbbed with migraines since being electrocuted in a freak accident a few weeks earlier. Prolonged staring at a computer screen only aggravated it, as did going outside in the blistering heat wave to perform any potential construction work. It felt like his brain was steaming like hot pavement. Physical pain aside, his mind was bothered by pulsating thoughts of his late mother's beautiful picture staring at him from a few feet away. His heart ached for possible pain relieving answers.

He knew he should've put the picture out of sight and mind and his growing depression would've perhaps alleviated, but he wanted to figure it out and dwell hard on it even if the tears he'd long been avoiding surfaced. He'd feel guilty if he put the photo away—like he'd abandoned her again. So he stared back at the photo's eyes in a hypnotized silence as he drank his beer. Then cracked another. And one more for good measure.

Andrew recalled how he had prayed silently for her death as she lay in the hospital. *No more pain for her, please.* And now he continued staring at the picture, tormented by those moments. He wondered if he had the conviction she'd make it like everyone else did, maybe it would have actually helped her pull through so their last conscious words to each other would've been, "I love you."

***

At the funeral Andrew read his eulogy about the well-respected woman on and off the Northern Cheyenne Indian reservation. "The Final Chapter," he called it, as "written by her writer son she'd been so proud of." He told of her genuine Christ-like behavior and willingness and readiness to help those less fortunate and deemed undesirable in society, filling it with Biblical scripture and real life anecdotes at the appropriate times. Afterward his pastor shook his hand, giving him the ultimate compliment from a Man of God: "I believe your calling was the ministry, young brother."

Although he was genuine in his belief if that there was a heaven she'd no doubt be the perfect candidate for it, he continually wondered if humanity's constant yearning and infatuation at the possibility of an afterlife was merely idle wishful thinking as he studied people walking past his mother's casket. He never cried, staying strong for the all the nieces and nephews and general children who knew her as the grandma who was genuinely interested in all of their little important stories that other adults were too busy to hear. Children wept not only out of sadness, but because it was contagious when they'd see an adult man or woman do the same as they'd never seen them do before, and they became scared. Andrew stayed strong for the people and his cousins who called her their second mom. He stayed strong for all of those that called his mom their best friend and sister.

He stayed strong for Vicki who also felt like she lost a second mom who still neutrally treated her like her own daughter even when she fought with her son. Vicki cried often on Andrew's mother's shoulder and through phone calls. She cried to her when he'd leave her all night and would shut off his phone and never answer her calls. She cried to her early on in their relationship when she saw him drink out of despair and hole up. Often while Vicki cried she'd tell her shared mutual feelings that she only wanted the best for Andrew's potential, but he illogically did things that would stunt that, like shun college as he seemingly preferred backbreaking construction labor followed by a dozen plus beers on paydays and in between with fellow construction working potheaded alkis to dull his physical and emotional aches.

A few years prior Andrew's mom was the matriarch and the one staying strong. On the day of the funeral of his little brother—her son—Andrew stayed in bed and stared at the ceiling, imagining that it was all a dream he'd wake up from as his little brother would soon shake him awake to tell him they needed to hurry up quick and get to the job site because shingles were being delivered and they needed to go unload them. If he didn't go to the funeral, there would be no end, no goodbyes —no poignant farewells. Not going to the funeral would somehow delay the harsh and inevitable full realization of it all.

"Come on, son," his mom said.

He didn't acknowledge her.

"It starts in 20 minutes," she said. "They'll all be waiting on you already."

No response.

"Hey," she said gently but with authority. He finally looked at her in the doorway, her desperate eyes watery and pleading. "Please," she said.

He couldn't exacerbate a mother's pain, felt selfish he had, and quickly got dressed.

Flash forward a couple of years, and his mom's cruel descent began with her diagnosis of a blood disease. Her pain was treated with powerful narcotics, and more narcotics were given to facilitate the side effects of those narcotics. She'd frequently end up in the hospital for days because of complications, and would only come out of the hospital with an even stronger dosage of pain relief. While the pills may have canceled out her physical pain, it also erased the characteristics of the person she once was.

She had good days and bad days—sometimes it was both. Once Andrew found an old t-shirt and hat of his little brothers in a closet and was wearing them proudly. He saw his mother pull up outside and she was already engaged in a conversation with the neighbor, playfully teasing him and laughing. The neighbor went inside. She beeped the horn to signal Andrew to come outside and grab his nephew—his deceased brother's son—to baby sit. He admired his mother through the curtain a few more seconds, honored he was the son of this full-blooded Northern Cheyenne woman with the glint of strong determination and warmth in her eyes that was enough to make anyone's day hopeful if they saw her.

He stepped outside and waved. She waved back and said with the brightest smile, "Hey-y-y!" before her face turned ashen as he came closer. "I...I'm sorry," she said. "I...I thought you were him. Your brother. The clothes...and..."

She looked almost embarrassed. "It's okay, mom," he said and gave her a strong hug. "I see him all the time, too."

He really did.

Hours later she came back to get her grandchild. He wouldn't let her drive home because she was loopy and her speech was slurred. She had taken one too many pills, and thus the cycle of mom always trying to meet up with her baby son via the afterlife began.

She was barely and rarely herself anymore after she divorced Andrew's dad and began drinking again after a hiatus of two dozen years, leaving her family behind to live off her Social Security in a small apartment that at times would turn into a flop house for local winos who'd take advantage of her generosity. Even in her stupors her nature was to help those in need; their nature was to leech off of her kindness and then beg for her last few dollars knowing she couldn't say no. Eventually, she stole money from family and sold powerful pills for more booze as well to supplement the winos and scam artists around her. Her family got tired of trying to help after having bridges to her burned, and could only watch from afar and hope for the best as the woman who once commanded so much respect in the community turned into a drunken mess.

Sensing her final setting sun, a month before her death Andrew pleaded with her to straighten up and go to treatment or at least detox.

Andrew texted her angry messages, frustrated with her drinking and the scamming drunks and addicts she'd surrounded herself with that shielded him from even bringing the inquiring grandchildren around to visit their grandma at her apartment. He wanted them to remember the strong and stubborn woman he'd grown up admiring, not the weak and beaten down alcoholic persona that had given up.

With tough love, he texted that she needed to stop being a wino. He rhetorically asked why she had a new loser boyfriend every other week that only wanted to steal her money. He heard he even beat her. He was going to kick that loser's ass, you watch.

She texted him back angrily as well, mocking him. She said his dad really wasn't his dad because she'd cheated on him with another half-breed Crow guy and he was the product.

Initially shocked at such seemingly brazen stupidity, he believed it to be the cruel ramblings of a delusional mind since he was her only child who resembled her white husband despite his darker skin. It pissed him off she could so disrespect an honorable man who still cared deeply for her welfare with such pointed words—he didn't care if she was drunk or angry or gone off of pills or not.

Don't ever talk to me again, whore, he typed in a fuming rage before blocking her nonsense.

***

Their last ugly messages to each other were still preserved in Andrew's phone history, and he stared at the words a long minute... maybe longer. Doubts about his DNA grew in his brain like a tumor. Maybe she was telling the truth and wanted to get it off her chest. Nah. Regardless, it was still an awful thing to say.

***

"She's not looking good," were the sometimes teary words he'd heard from his dad and others who'd just recently seen her. He thought of making one last plea to her even personally to her face. *Please, at least sober up long enough to make yourself presentable for the grandchildren,* he'd say. He'd look down at his phone to text or maybe even call her to make sure she was there, but bitterness from the words about his dad not being his biological father would prevail, despite how much he missed her. She could only help herself at that point, and she didn't want to. It all accumulated with a final ambulance ride after Andrew's sister/cousin (his mom's niece) called 9-11.

She had coughed up plenty of blood two days before her death— right before she lost consciousness. Hooked up to machines that performed the functions required for her to live, her fragile failing body and mind had by then already given up, but the doctor said there was still a small chance she'd pull through. Andrew knew she only wanted to go see her youngest baby son in heaven, and death's door was too inviting as the warm light inside beckoned a reprieve from the cold world. Truthfully, at times, that's something Andrew wanted to do as well during darker days: go to that door with the final answer for all of life's mysteries and miseries. This time he knew she hurt too badly, not just emotionally, but physically as well. Andrew prayed for her death and her pain to cease so she could sleep forever in peace. It truly wasn't a nefarious intention despite their last conversation.

As his mom slept in a comatose state he wondered if she could even dream while he held her warm hand which trembled every so often. People streamed in and out of the ICU room and shed unapologetic tears.

All prayed with their eyes closed tight and with the utmost confidence she'd pull through. The steady humming of the breathing mechanism forced her chest to move up and down. More blood trickled from the side of her lips. He wiped it and only wanted to unplug the machine and let her soul escape from the prison that had become her body. Her soul did just that the next morning, two days before her grandson's late January birthday.

As Andrew shook hands and comforted his grieving family and friends at the funeral, he noticed a black man he'd seen a couple of times years ago when his mom worked at the Mission. He was one of many whose lives had been bettered by knowing his mother. He recalled when his mother spoke of him she'd noted he was "kind of not all there in the head," but nonetheless had a good heart and she brought him to The Lord and saved him as she prayed with the repenting and tearful man in an alley one windy day outside the Mission. Andrew went to shake the man's hand and tell him thank you for coming, and he was truly sorry that his friend—or his own mother— that never judged him and always had a kind word for him had passed.

The man spoke to him first with words that would forever echo in his soul, however. "You're her son Andrew, right?"

He nodded.

"Yeah, good, good!" he said. "Your mom kept talking about you all the time. I kept waiting to meet you. She kept saying it all last week when I saw her and visited her—said you were coming. Cuz I had a feeling something wasn't right and she didn't look too good so I went and saw her, you know? But she said, 'My son is going to come visit me today. My son is gonna come visit me today!' She said the same thing two days later when I went and checked on her again. Then she went to the hospital that night, I heard. Did you take her? Anyway, I kept looking forward to meeting you because she was so excited about you—just bragging about how proud she was of her boy—you know? And now I'm glad to finally meet you!"

***

Andrew cried for the first time in years. He had to sit up and put his beer down because the held in tears came out like a desert cloudburst on his arid soul accompanied by guttural sobs that made it difficult to even breathe. He said, "Why didn't I go see you, mom? But...why did you tell me that about dad. Fuck, why?"

He kissed his mom's image on the forehead, hugged it, and consciously forgave her again for the first time since the hospital. He even apologized out loud. He wouldn't wake up until hours later as Vicki screamed at him, telling him to get the hell out because his daughter didn't need to see him like that. Ever again. He barely heard Vicki's voice. He didn't blame her for anything though, and it'd be pointless to explain. Since their vehicle was in Vicki's name, Andrew hitchhiked out of the Indian reservation border town of Hardin, Montana and ended up at a friend's house some 40 miles away back in his hometown of Billings.

He called Vicki the next day and told her he picked up a decent check for freelance writing from his permanent mailing address in town. He wanted to buy his daughter some more Head Start school clothes. Pay the rent. She told him she didn't give a fuck, they didn't need his help, and he should never call back again. He drank for three days alone in a motel following. During that time Vicki made a special trip just to dump off his clothes at his dad's.

A month or so later things calmed down and he was allowed to see his daughter again early on a Friday night. At the former place he called home resentment hung in the air but they chatted anyway to kill the tension as Vicki caught him up on the various rez gossip while their daughter jovially ran back and forth between them, not understanding why daddy had left her for so long but simply happy he was there with mommy once again. "Mommy...daddy! Mommy...daddy!" she'd proudly say and point at each of them with a gleaming smile and tilted head.

That night, Andrew asked if it was possible if they could let bygones be bygones and if they could start over again as a texting Vicki lay on the bed that they'd made so much uninhibited love on. He tried rubbing her back because he knew it was always bothering her, but she pushed his hand away roughly and said, "Just...don't."

"But why?" he said.

That's when she told him she didn't love him anymore.

"I'm going out and I'll stay at my cousin's," Vicki said as she put on her lipstick an hour later. "I'll be back in the morning, and I'll take you home when I get back," she smacked her lips.

God, she looked so wonderfully beautiful to him. He wished he could take her pic, and he regretted all he'd done and the things he'd put her through for at least the thousandth time.

For a few weeks this went on as he watched his daughter a few hours on Friday nights. They'd go to the park before it got dark, do puzzles, draw together, maybe watch a movie, and read before she fell asleep on his arm. He'd cuddle close to her, listening to her tiny breaths. Soft tears would come down every time he thought of his baby's pain of missing her daddy, even overriding his own misery. He'd make his daughter her favorite pancake breakfast in the morning, and she'd ask the whole time where mommy was.

"Staying the night at a *cousin's* house—one of your aunties," he'd say, trying not to let sarcasm slip into his voice while flipping a cake, attempting in vain to put up a facade that hid his depression and deep want for everything to just go back to how it was so he could enjoy the couple more hours left of her presence until the next week. After breakfast he'd walk with her to the gas station store to buy her anything she wanted—ice cream even. Vicki would generally arrive around 11:30, acting overly aggressive about everything. Previously, Andrew encouraged her to go out with friends when possible so she could blow off steam and have a good time. Now, instead of coming back speaking of fun times and karaoke songs sung, Vicki came back venting her steam at his very existence it seemed. While giving him a ride home she'd put on a top 40 radio station that she knew annoyed him and blast it loud so they wouldn't be able to talk. The child would stare at her daddy with a bewildered look the entire 30 minute drive to Billings, only knowing daddy wouldn't be there at least for the rest of the day and more and not understanding why. "See you next week!" he'd say and hug her, but she did not understand what "week" meant.

To her tiny lifespan, not seeing her daddy for six more nights might as well have been a year.

***

Before Andrew's mom had gotten sober for some two decades and lived a life of legit righteousness, she'd leave the house and go on alcoholic benders for days or weeks and leave Andrew and his little brother and father to fend for themselves up until he was about eight. Although Andrew's father worked hard, he'd still travel nearly every other summer night or weekend to take them fly fishing to keep his mind off of the fact his wife was gone. In the winter he'd take them skiing a lot—mostly cross-country because it was free. Andrew started to become annoyed by fishing itself because he got sick of eating trout.

Still, he always loved the solitude and nature of it all as his dad would travel to the Bighorn River on the Crow Indian Reservation to the southeast, or the high elevation Beartooth Mountains to the west. His little brother loved it as well, apparently, because later as a young man he'd venture on weeks-long backpacking trips across the Continental Divide amidst many other places "still no white man had ever been," he'd joke.

When running through the more immediate steep and rolling hills behind his home as a child, Andrew always imagined he was the great Lakota runner and Olympic Champion Billy Mills. While playing sports or drawing as a kid, he didn't have to think of how his mother wasn't at home—or when she'd be back.

Once when he was his six, his little brother who was four-and-a-half stared at him with watery eyes from the hallway as Andrew put his camouflage shirt and pants on. His brother looked like he was going to cry. Their mom had been gone for about two weeks that time. "Are you hurt?" Andrew asked.

His brother shook his head no, but he was. "Where's mom at?" He started to cry, and through his pain said, "I don't want her to be gone any-*more*! I want her to come back home and cook me mac-a-*roni*!"

It wasn't a loud cry after his sentence, but it was such a powerful one that it gave Andrew goose bumps. Andrew wanted to join him because he felt the same, but he couldn't. He knew he had to be tough. He told his little brother there was nothing to worry about while rubbing his back like he'd seen his mom always do to comfort him.

Although he didn't see it as bad thing, Andrew knew he couldn't be sensitive anymore. He'd learned to read well early, and dug up the meaning of the word 'sensitive' in a thick dictionary when he'd heard the phrase 'sensitive artist.' From his understanding, it kind of meant you had a lot of feelings and would cry easily, but it also meant you were caring about things. He wanted to be a sensitive artist and care deeply, but he didn't want to cry. He'd fold pieces of paper together and draw books on them—usually scenes of war or dinosaurs fighting or basic cartoon adventures. He wanted to be the best artist, but reasoned if he were sensitive, he'd just have to cry on the inside from then on and be tough.

"She'll come back, I promise," he said.

"When?" his brother demanded.

"I...don't know. She'll come back though. She always does, remember?" He helped his little brother up off of the hallway floor. "Come on, bud. We were supposed to go shoot some birds with the BB gun, 'member?"

Shooting their BB gun at something was something tough guys would do, and they were extremely efficient at it. He was proud he never cried as this similar scenario would play itself out several times during the next week that summer before mom finally came home and slept for two days.

***

While working on a fresh magazine article, Andrew contacted a self-proclaimed local gay Native American rights activist via Facebook message. The article would be about, of course, Native Americans, and their seemingly ironic modern and conservative-based intolerance for gays when historically tribes had no such qualms against homosexuals. To Natives all around North America, it was the introduction of Christianity that made homosexuals–or Two Spirits–who were once deemed natural and even supernatural—become unnatural. Unlike most people who eagerly spoke to him at the mention of the popular news magazine he often worked on behalf of, this activist who should have seemingly craved the exposure for the cause seemed cautious, and suddenly Vicki had unblocked him on Facebook to message, *Why the fuck are you bothering my friends????*

Because I'm doing an article, psycho. Geez, he messaged back right away. *Jokes you're not a psycho. I'm so Sorry! How are you?*

He felt like a jerk. He missed chatting with her so bad. While he honestly theorized she had some sort of mood disorder she was too stubborn to admit to and perhaps needed medication for, he also knew she hated being called psycho even if she unreasonably acted like one for days at a time despite obviously strained efforts to try to calm herself. Not many people wanted to admit they were somehow broken, however—whereas Andrew at least could admit his heart needed serious mending. Days of her irrational anger would often be preceded or proceeded by days of uptempo and jovial behavior that seemed to develop a radiant, positive life aura of its own. Those were the days Andrew fondly chose to recall the most when he thought of her, days of blissful harmony and inner warmth that seemed destined in their lives forever....

Oh, is all she replied.

While messaging with the activist, he had the distinct feeling that Vicki and her friend were texting back and forth as well. *Just curious, but is your friend gay?* Andrew texted Vicki. Vicki texted, *Lmao! Oh no, he's not.* The activist texted, *I'm not gay, by the way. Lol. I have a couple of friends and relatives that are though.* Andrew texted in a PC manner, *It wouldn't matter if you were.*

It went on like that, and Andrew felt it odd she'd been so defensive of him. Previously, when he mentioned he'd eventually do an article about gays in the Native American community, she scoffed at the idea because she was in a bad mood and it was a week before she kicked him out and was "growing tired of his shit." Oh well, he had the information and contacts he needed and thanked the activist. He seemed like a good-hearted guy who genuinely wanted to help in the culture wars against discrimination behind the scenes.

The week before Vicki's birthday Andrew typed out a carefully contemplative and lengthy email letter on his phone, once again sincerely apologizing for all the wrongs he'd done. It took him two late nights lying in bed to write it with plenty of tears between sentences. The tears he'd avoided for so long became routine during silent nights as he longed for his child and love.

He wrote that he respected Vicki and fully understood why she grew fed up with him, but please understand that was truly not him as a person. That was the gist of what he wrote. He wrote he was good guy and never meant to take her for granted, he was going through so much and he was just too afraid to tell anyone lest it be concluded as conceding defeat to his inner-demons. He even confessed the news about what his mom said about his father, how embarrassing it was, and that's what had been bothering him so much; that's why he'd been so distant about pretty much everything leading up to their last breakup.

He wrote he finally cried for the first time since his mother died that day she kicked him out. He wrote he mostly regretted he wasn't brave enough to trust the woman he'd considered his soulmate about the blackness enveloping his tired soul, and perhaps they would still be together if he'd gotten it off his chest and their relationship would've grown stronger and not so fragile that it shattered for it. He never mentioned he was afraid to talk to her because she'd grown so cold to him, as he didn't want to come off as pointing fingers in a genuine apology.

And also, he still thought she was truly the most beautiful woman inside and out in the world. Did she know her face was still his phone wallpaper? There was no way he could understate how much he appreciated her, how much he genuinely loved her, how boastful he still was of her. Proud of his perfectly crafted sentiments, he saved the letter in an email message and would send it while he watched their daughter on Friday night which was two days before Vicki's birthday—her favorite day of the year. Perhaps he'd get a genuine hug after she read it, and at least a semblance of healing could hopefully begin.

The morning after she read the letter, she slammed the door open. "Get the fuck out of my house, right now!" she said.

"Jeez! Why? I'm still paying for it, too! I'm on the lease. No need to be rude."

"I don't give a fuck. I said I want you out!"

"Why?"

"Because you're a fucking asshole, that's why! You just sent that letter just to play some guilt game and ruin and fuck up my entire night and birthday! If you don't get out right fucking now, I'm calling the cops to escort you out!"

His daughter began to tear up, wishing Mommy wouldn't be so upset at her Daddy anymore, remembering and wishing they'd laugh and laugh together like they used to. He gave her a smile as if to tell her it was okay, but the little girl knew it wasn't okay as she saw Daddy's pained and panicked eyes in a scene that would be forever etched into her mind. Baby knew there wouldn't even be that sad ride to take Daddy home that day. "Bye, Baby," he said and gave her a rueful hug and kiss before walking out the door on a sunny November morning, a feeling of wanting to faint clouding his vision.

"Six fucking wasted years! I fucking hate you!" she yelled as he reached the end of the block and turned.

***

He gave her room for a couple of weeks after she ignored his calls for a few days. He'd got tired of listening to different angry break up ringtone songs emanating from her phone before it would inform him that her voice mailbox was full. But after those couple of weeks he knew he had to fight to see his daughter if anything—especially when he heard she'd given up the house they rented to move back to the Crow Indian Reservation where she could plan to save money and finish her advanced degree at the University of Montana, 400 plus miles away in

Missoula. He began calling and texting her a few times a day, sometimes pleadingly, sometimes angrily while typing things like, *What the fuck??? The kid didn't do anything you don't have to use baby as a hostage! She loves her daddy, just because you don't...*

Finally late one night she finally called him back. "Why the fuck are you trying to blow up my phone, psycho? You need to leave me the fuck alone and get on with your life. Get it through your head that I'm finished with you."

Andrew said, "Dude, we have a kid together. I'm not like the rest of those deadbeat morons on the rez who pop out kids and care less if they see them again. I know you want me to be that way to make it easier to play victim—go around telling everyone I'm a deadbeat drunk—but it's not in my blood. Baby is in my blood."

"I'm getting full custody," she said. "The only reason I let you watch her before was because I needed a babysitter to go fuck someone else not you. You couldn't even get it hard the last time I even tried to have sex with you."

She hung up.

In spite of the piercing words that were probably true and as much as he wanted to bite her bait and slut shame her, he only frantically texted her back, pleading they should at least act civilized about their child. He thought he made great points, all of them unarguable if one used common sense—even the part about being too depressed to have sex the last time. But it didn't matter and she knew she held the upper hand. All she'd have to do to keep him away from his daughter was tell the tribal court he was a remedial alcoholic who needed treatment. She could show them unanswered text messages one could construe as verbally abusive if taken out of the context that he was fighting for his daughter and was tired of asking nicely.

She knew the tribal judge and lawyers personally, and it'd take months for him just to get signed up for a tribal outpatient treatment program, and it would take the same amount of time to finish. Fuck him after all of those psycho texts, Vicki thought, as well as that letter he sent just to screw with her mind right before her birthday of all days just to make her feel guilty. She would win the break up.

Andrew didn't want to win any break up. He wanted to see his daughter and saw his chances fast slipping away. He'd give Vicki space and a little time again anyhow while he wondered how many times a day "My Daddy!" crossed his daughter's mind.

Later that week after his article about Natives and gays came out, Andrew recalled how he got some of the sources. It hit him like a brick upside the head: That activist was the one she'd been going out with.

He wasn't naive to think Vicki wouldn't try to get laid if she kept going out while he watched their child—as she so rudely said. Nor did it seem plausible that a 32-year-old woman needed to spend her entire night out at a "friend's house" every Friday as if it were a slumber party. Besides, she rarely even drank.

He recalled her extreme defensiveness when he contacted the guy, plus how the guy was acting nervous even over instant messages. Vicki always came home right after check out time from the local motel. They both had him blocked from Facebook. The activist's blocking of him was especially peculiar, and he only realized it after he was going message to thank him and tell him the article was out.

He could've figured it out earlier had he been more cynical, but his hopefulness became his disillusionment. He simply didn't want to believe she was with another man. Why was she so flippant immediately after he sent that heartfelt letter that weekend? It was because she was with *him* and felt guilty for whatever reasons. As was Vicki's common practice, she went on the offensive rather than defensive whenever a guilty conscious threatened, only that time it was on a severe level that caused her to not let him see his daughter since.

Tired of playing nice, Andrew realized his not seeing his daughter was related indirectly to the other guy. She'd gotten pissed that morning because she woke up next to *him*. She got pissed because perhaps she was supposed to hang out with *him* on her birthday and her mood would be altered with a burdened conscience. Speculation, perhaps, but Andrew was tired of playing stupid and the palpable vision of some squirrely schmuck giving her a back massage sent him over.

While a seeming knife pierced his heart and he gushed crimson, he texted his bloody words to her. *So the guy I was asking the questions to about sources for the article, that article that came out the other day...he was the one, huh?*

What are you talking about? Who have you been talking to?

No one. I can deduct your whorish behavior on my own.

He presented his evidence in a flurry of thumb typing.

She wrote, *Alright! So I'm busted? So what? We're not even together and it's none of your fucking business anymore what I do.*

You probably slept with him while we were together. Gross. That's messed up.

LMAO! I actually waited until a week after we broke up since you think you know all of my business.

That meant she'd been in contact with him prior to that. Fuck that fucking home wrecker asshole, he thought. Yeah, Andrew wasn't an angel but she was extreme and no wonder the guy somehow seemed nervous even through the safety of the internet. *How noble of you to wait a week. *eye roll* Is that some kind of Floozy Code of Honor?*

What are you from the 50's? Floozy? Really???

It heatedly boiled into madness until all she'd write was *Fuck you* and *Go to hell.*

***

She was busted and fuming with fresh rage, but wouldn't let him win the breakup. She still held the card that was his child and would use it because fuck him; who she screwed was none of his damn business. If he'd cared so much now about his daughter, he shouldn't have been such a fuck up in the first place.

Her revenge would be to leave him cold turkey again and not even call him lest his admittedly familiar calming voice play her heart that twitched towards him as if it were a soothing familiar sirenic tune, much to her annoyance. It wasn't his right to pass discernment in regards to what she did in her own free time. Like he should judge when he'd randomly leave them every few weeks to go out drinking at God knows where all night and not come back until the next day acting like nothing happened, pretending like she wasn't up all night literally worrying herself sick with anxiety attacks.

During the first year after she gave birth, Andrew and his bonehead cousin had gotten in a major wreck while out drinking. The cause of the wreck technically wasn't their fault as the semi-truck they clipped had failed to stop at a sign. It made them spin like a top after totaling the entire front end. After seeing the mangled wreck of the vehicle the next day, Vicki was frozen in fear and cried knowing how close the man she loved had come to dying. Because of his habitual seat belt use, he'd somehow survived with barely some scratches from shattered glass and mild whiplash; his cousin ended up with broken bones and a week long stay in the hospital, but nothing too serious. She'd cry alone in bed at nights when he didn't come back, thinking the worst and picturing that mangled car. Vicki thought Andrew still had no idea what he'd put her through all these years: screw apology letters that came way too late.

Then she started seeing him getting worse with his drinking *again* and acting like it was normal? There was no way she could let her daughter grow up around the type of stress she'd been through.

Enough was enough.

For several days his desperate text messages came in. She'd show her friends at work. They'd have a laugh together. "Stupid drunken idiot," they'd say. "No means, no!" They'd laugh again. They didn't know exactly what it was about Andrew, but Vicki's friends had always disliked the quiet weirdo with his so-called 'off-beat' sense of sarcastic humor they only wanted to roll their eyes at when he spoke. They knew Vicki deserved someone who was more outgoing and personable like her, not some closet alcoholic wannabe hermetic bohemian writer as they thought of him—and that was on a nice day. On mean days, well...it wasn't pretty the clever names they'd come up with to bash him especially now that Vicki could join them.

Andrew's desperate messages started getting angrier. He questioned her motives for not letting him see their child and even attacked her new boyfriend. *Did that asshole tell you not to let me see my kid? Fuck that guy. Fuck you too for cheating on me with that home wrecker.*

It again got under Vicki's skin that he dared judge her love life. She finally texted back, *Fuck you! You don't even know about us and how could I cheat when we were not together, idiot??? Besides I'm not even with that guy anymore not that it's any of your business! Get on with your pathetic wannabe loser writer life.*

Oh, that get on your nerves? Must have if it made you stop ignoring me. It is my business if that guy sees my daughter more than I do.

Bye. I'm done. Stop harassing me now. Again, get on with your own life and stop trying to ruin mine.

Me trying to see my daughter is 'harassing' now??? That's sound logic. YEAH. Go post another man-hater meme or long-winded diatribe about horrible alcoholic men for sympathetic Facebook likes to make yourself feel like a superior victim.

He texted a few more stupid theories about "her new boyfriend"—who really wasn't as their relationship was not public and only a few of Vicki's closest friends even knew about it. It was so-o-o annoying that

Andrew had somehow figured it out. Anyway, hooked up in bland marriages themselves, Vicki's friends loved, swooned, and lived vicariously through her when she gushed about fresh details of her new man, sometimes squealing like tweens with crushes on pop singers when he'd sneakily do romantic stuff like leave her chocolates and flowers on her desk. It was so James Bond and sexy, they said. For several weeks the gleam in her eye that only those with a love of life possessed returned to Vicki when she thought about him, but she also rolled those same eyes whenever a fresh text or email message from Andrew came in—not even bothering to check them anymore. No longer did she feel alone even in crowds. For several weeks she was back to her witty, clever self and was the sparkle that illuminated an entire room once again.

But after awhile—unbeknownst to her closest friends—her new man hadn't contacted her back enthusiastically in like a week since she announced to him that Andrew was onto them, just relaying fake *lol*'s and dismissive *oh* answers. He'd been acting increasingly strange right before that, even acting annoyed when she had to bring her daughter along to meet up with him for dinner dates. She felt perhaps he was already looking for an excuse to bail, and Andrew was it.

Fuck men, Vicki thought. She didn't need her daughter around any of those worthless assholes who could only serve to disappoint. She glanced at Andrews last 20 or so messages she'd ignored. Most of them had become increasingly angry. Good. They looked like the ramblings of a psychopath. *I was good enough to watch her while you were out being a fucking whore, and now I'm suddenly not???* She smiled and thought, nope, you're not. After she presented the text evidence on her phone to the tribal police, she was granted a restraining order immediately a week before Christmas. She'd bury him in this breakup, plus he'd pay for ruining her new relationship, no doubt.

***

Five days before Christmas Andrew wrote a lengthy email once again apologizing for all of his behavior, but not taking full blame this time because it was fucked what she was doing to their child's mind in making her believe Daddy abandoned her without a word.

Plus, when she last did talk and text to him the last few times she said some pretty messed up and degrading shit to him he ignored at the time. He also needed to get it off his chest that whatever she told everyone on Facebook or wherever about him wasn't cool. He was a private person with a respected journalist byline. He recounted to her how he walked into a grocery store while working construction down on the Crow Rez and a couple of seemingly random people flipped him off as he bought lunch and called him an asshole. Her Facebook friends, perhaps?

Sympathetic people who were neutral would sometimes relay messed up things she'd posted about him on Facebook, saying things like, "I know you guys are having a messed up child custody dispute, but *still,* man, I know that kid loves you. She shouldn't be putting you on blast like that. It's bullshit women always have to throw kids into it first thing then then cry to everyone it's all one-hundred percent the dad's fault even when it's a stand up guy that actually wants his kids. Society eats that shit up too, man."

Andrew's friends saw their friend grow more secluded emotionally and shun that same society the longer he hadn't seen his daughter. What was it like, two months now? They were genuinely pained that one of the coolest and smartest guys they knew could be put through the ringer like that in regards to his daughter for no real logical point. They'd call Vicki a bitch and cunt.

Through it all, Andrew would still stick up for her publicly. "Nah, she's a good woman," he'd say. "I'm pissed about the kid, but Vicki... she's got a good heart. She's just mad, and I'm not innocent either. She just needs to vent. Like...even probably the people who 'like' her

Facebook rants and memes against me have never talked to me anyway in real life, so fuck 'em. She'll come around. Maybe we can work it out."

They'd shake their heads, baffled at how he could still stand up for her. "Fuck that, dude. You didn't do anything wrong to lose your daughter. I've seen her around you. All she does is hug you. That's fucking bullshit what she's doing—jus' sayin'."

Vicki never answered his apology the whole next day. Fine then, he figured. He got to his main point the next night: *Look, it's a few days until Christmas, and I want to make amends as we can't have our baby not seeing her daddy of all things on Christmas. I'm tired of being angry, and I'm sure you are by now, too. I'll be on the rez on Christmas Eve. I have to do a small job down there—like a favor practically since I'll make so little money—then I'll drop off a present. I'll have more presents at my dad's house though. She needs to see her other family. Her cousin misses her and asks about her every day.*

Surely, the magic of Christmas would override any remaining harsh feelings, Andrew thought. He felt positive he'd see his daughter at least maybe after Christmas if anything. There was so much fun they'd have. He texted Vicki and said he was on his way over after installing a new front door on an elderly Native woman's home. The previous door had been busted down when her house was broken into and her TV was stolen. Stupid meth heads.

I'll be there in 5 minutes. It's just a Berenstain Bear cartoon Christmas variety DVD she can watch to get into the spirit, you know? Lol. I'll just leave it by the front door and leave. You won't even have to see me if it makes you uncomfortable, but as always if you need some extra $$$ just ask. Just got paid a few journalism checks. Been writing a ton, dude! But yeah please do let me know holiday plans, and tell baby Daddy loves her! And I love you as well, always. xoxox

He dropped off the present, his co-worker pulled out of the driveway, and they saw a pair of police lights. What they hell did they do? It couldn't be serious, as they were both sober and the driver had never so much as jaywalked in his life. The tribal police asked if Andrew was in the passenger seat. Affirmative.

"Can you step out the vehicle, please? You're under arrest for violating a restraining order," the officer said. "You know you're not supposed to harass that young lady Vicki anymore. She called us and said you were on your way over."

He slapped on the handcuffs. Andrew said that wasn't true, and he didn't even know there was a restraining order. They asked if he was served one, and he told them he knew he and Vicki were having problems, but nothing that would warrant a restraining order. He was dropping off a present of all things and on his way back to Billings, he said. They actually believed his truth and felt bad they had to arrest him while they kept saying "they had to go by the book"—especially in the shadow of the recently passed Violence Against Woman Act federal law. What really bothered the police, however, was Andrew wouldn't be able to address the judge until after Christmas weekend on Monday and it was only Thursday. His bail would likely be set at $500 that he'd have to pay in full if he wanted to get out.

His friend and ride said he'd get him out ASAP. "Don't bother," Andrew said. "I can get myself out when I get there and get my own ride. I got a lot of money right now. I'll get a room later. Go home and enjoy your family, please."

He pondered his strategy on the way to the tribal jail. Sure he flipped out under extenuating circumstances of her probably illegally keeping his daughter from him, but he never threatened her physically or anything despite all of that. If harassment equated wanting to see a daughter on Christmas and calling someone on their bullshit who held a child from a father for no discernible reason other than revenge, then call him guilty. At least that's what he'd tell the judge eventually, but not right away because he'd plead innocent and fight the case to the death.

They put him in a large cell with double bunks lining the wall with some 15 other Indians, a mixture of old drunks and young hyper and usually tweeker punks. Jail wasn't anything particularly new to Andrew, but it'd thankfully been a few years since he'd last seen the inside of one and this was his first time in this particular Crow tribal one. At booking they counted his money: $1,122. They asked him if he was sure he didn't want to bail himself out.

"It's Christmas!" they kept saying as if the words meant anything to him then.

He grumbled negative. He wanted to say fuck Christmas.

He slept as long as he could to stave off his depression on Christmas morning, only getting up to grab his breakfast to give it to an old guy before going back to sleep until noon. As he ate lunch curious people asked the usual Indian jailhouse questions: What tribe are you? Who's your family? Where do you live? What's your charge? He watched TV for an hour before going back to the quieter cell area where most people tried to nap or read. He looked through the magazines and thought an old National Geographic would do the trick to get his mind off the fact it was Christmas. On his way to his bunk he noticed another inmate was reading a magazine he'd recently written a lengthy feature piece in.

"Hey," he said as he approached a man of about 25-years-old.

"Yeah, what's up?"

"That magazine you have...let me show you something in there."

"Sure, whatever, I was just looking at the pictures! Erbz!"

Andrew flipped to his article and pointed underneath the headline. "See that name? That's me."

He wasn't being braggadocio or anything, he just thought it'd be interesting to the guy. He showed him his court ordered restraining order with the matching name.

"Holy shit!" he exclaimed more excitedly than Andrew expected. "That *is* you!"

After shaking Andrew's hand, he went to the TV room and showed off to everyone that the guy they were bunking with was a guy who'd written in that one famous magazine. He shit them not.

Baffled and amused inmates asked Andrew questions beyond the generalities. They asked why he, "a famous writer" according to them, stayed in that shithole during Christmas when he could get out whenever he wanted. The trustee had seen them unload a fat stack of cash when they booked him, after all. He just said he didn't have any place to go, nor could he see his daughter if he did. They accepted his answer as fair enough—although still pretty stupid, just go get drunk!— then wondered how a man with a supposedly prestigious title that labeled him smart was still committed to a vindictive woman who obviously hated him if she had him thrown in there on Christmas.

"Fuck, that's messed up," one old guy pondered and shook his head with a toothless grin. "Dropping off a present? Shit dat's rough! Your old lady will have Santa Claus thrown in here with us guys tonight, I bet! Ho-lay!"

Everyone laughed. "Yeah well, the only reason I want to stay with her is because I'm a creepy stalker according to these charges. Like that *Twilight* movie guy. All I was doing was digging through her garbage! Jokes!" Andrew said. "Fuck, it *is* bullshit. Fucking cop caller from hell and I didn't even do anything but play Santa Claus. Wanted to see my kid, man."

His own foolish commitment aside, the actual practice of monogamy seemed to baffle most of these tribal members in spite of their long having the highest percentage of self-proclaimed Christians among Natives in the region, Andrew thought. When they got angry, they cheated—especially younger couples who treated it as a rite of passage to do so. Other Montana tribes had long joked about their alleged promiscuity. Vicki even admitted she'd cheated on Andrew —'chippying around' as the Blackfeet up north called it—three years ago and never did apologize for it. Not apologizing out of stubbornness because 'he'd been out drinking again' always messed with Andrew's head, and he always thought of it when he was especially mad at her— like right then when he was in jail because of her. Andrew recalled Robert Redford's *Jeremiah Johnson* movie that had given this particular tribe heavy praise for being great warriors and horsemen as told by a veteran mountain man, but he ended his sentiments by calling them "...an adulterous people. *Adulterous*." Not that the reputation stemmed only from the film, as one famed ethnologist had noted they were regarded as the most 'dissolute' of Plains tribes in relationship and love matters and stereotypes had to stem from somewhere, Andrew thought much to his hardened and personal dismay right then. Still, he culpably knew it was emotionally immature to lump summate an entire peoples based on his personal happenings—especially since his daughter was partly of the tribe.

Although Andrew mostly grew up on the outskirts of the non-reservation hub city of Billings, as a southeastern Montana Native he was very familiar experience-wise with this tribe since they were the closest one in the area. Plus, most whites viewed Indians as a conglomerate and usually assumed he was Crow as well although he didn't really resemble their generally lanky physicalities. Andrew's Northern Cheyenne tribe—with an adjoining reservation border located some 30 miles east—was also markedly divergent in many other ways in regards to their historic rival Crow tribe. Whereas the Crow deemed it impolite to casually speak at length about recently deceased loved ones, his tribe oft spoke fondly of them as if they were still alive as to respect their memory.

As a matter of practicality to fend off the encroachment of enemy tribes outnumbering them, the Crow eventually allied with the U.S.

During the 1860's Plains Indian Wars, their scouting and fighting involvement kept U.S. soldiers—fresh from fighting the Civil War and ill-suited for Indian fighting—on the Montana and Wyoming Territory's Bozeman Trail longer than Lakota's Red Cloud and Crazy Horse as well as Cheyenne like Roman Nose would've otherwise allowed. This was most pointedly proven by the nullification of Captain Fettermen's dubious claim that "with 80 men I could ride right through the Sioux Nation." The end result of Fetterman and his 80 men was called the Fettermen Massacre—or Battle of the 100 Slain—and a resounding victory for Indian tribes that would lead to a U.S. retreat at the end of what was called Red Cloud's War. The ill-fated and soon-to-be-broken Fort Laramie Treaty of 1868, that promised large swaths of the Northern Plains to the victorious tribes, would result and war would eventually flare up again during which General Custer would ride his fame to historical infamy.

The Cheyenne, who had formerly always encouraged peace with the whites at any cost, had ironically bore the brunt of some of the most brutally unprovoked blood baths in history on U.S. soil like at Sand Creek in 1864 and then the Custer-oriented Washita River Massacre in 1868. They'd always be deemed renegades afterward for having had the audacity to actually defend themselves against such ruthless onslaughts as they aligned with tribes at war with the whites.

In addition to having to fend off the powerful and continually raiding Blackfeet, the Crow—or Apsaalooke as they call themselves—battled against so-called "hostile" and allied Lakota, Cheyenne, and Arapaho tribes on their own traditional lands. Battles took a toll on them just as smallpox epidemics did a few decades prior when their numbers went from—by some estimates—about 8,000 to about half of that from the late 1830's to the early 1850's. Crow casualties in war parties that previously had numbered just a few at most in small skirmishes would by the 1870's turn to dozens at times as every hill, mountain, and river valley was fiercely fought over in attempts garner some of the last prime game-infested areas alongside the Rocky Mountains and Northern Plains. As a result, some veteran mountain men traders predicted the Crow could very well become extinct.

Those anti-white allied tribes, of course, also stoutheartedly battled soldiers and cavalry from the east and south in their own desperate bids for survival. Their lands had already been flooded by settlers after various broken peace treaties, while the bison lifeline in those areas were decimated at the encouragement and behest of the U.S. Government in efforts to halt their "savage" nomadic ways that'd eventually confine them to reservations.

When Custer was killed after attacking the Cheyenne side of the camp at the Battle of the Little Bighorn, the allied defending "hostile" tribes celebrated whilst the Crow mourned hard. The Crow didn't mourn because of the loss of the dead white soldier chief, but because there was a massively victorious occupying force in the middle of the very sacred lands they'd already lost so much warriors and blood fighting for.

Another difference was the Cheyenne tribe traditionally took great pride in their monogamy, Andrew again spitefully pondered as he tried to block out the knowing feeling and fact Vicki's new guy had seen his daughter far more than he had in the last several months.

Andrew had outgrown visiting party houses–save for when he would drink for a night or so at a bachelor pad with one of his few friends, of course–while those were the foremost places most of these jailhouse guys would go when released. In that, the types of women these dudes hooked up with where for the most part leery of even being with a guy like Andrew. Those sketchy party women would literally brawl over people like Andrew's ex-con cousins, however. His cousins often tried to hook him up with Native party gals when he was single— even recently to help him feel better about losing Vicki—bragging that their cuz Andrew was a writer, showing off his articles on their phones from the internet. Andrew would smile and know what was coming: they'd immediately be leery he'd somehow include them in an article for their vices as if he were an undercover informant who gave a shit. Sometimes it was just their meth thinking, but a stint in prison was more impressive than a byline to them. While they could get at least a few wilder women to choose from, Andrew probably couldn't even get an old wino hag if he was desperate. Sometimes, because of his good looks and a lack of game combined with his studious shyness and what rez girls said was a white accent, they even assumed he was gay. Some Indians who lived back and forth from the rez to the city developed two accents as to not stand out where they were at the time, although Andrew noticed seriously strong rez accents were getting less frequent among younger people.

Likewise, the intellectual-type women Andrew strove for would never go with these bad boys—nor Andrew now, apparently. Well, most of these inmates weren't particularly bad people in this tribal jail that wasn't used for hardcore criminals save for perhaps maybe a brief holding period before transporting them off to federal custody if they were a felon. They'd just got caught doing dumb shit one too many times deserving of a long enough stint in that even the judge wouldn't let them out on their own recognizance in time for Christmas. Perhaps they got drunk and fought their girlfriends, had dope in their pockets, drove while having one too many, or did all three in a night.

Once comfortable in Andrew's presence, they of course started impersonally teasing their short timer Cheyenne cellmate because that's what Indians did when they liked you and knew you wouldn't respond like a douche bag.

"Dis guy Andrew right here, only staying here cuz he's really gonna write a magazine story up about me being bad ass. Front page cover! Agu-u-ah!"

"Yup...come all the way from Bill-ings, but only cuz he's doin' an undercover story about how you got raped in here—and liked it! Prolly for a hardcore beat freak gay mag."

"Aw-w-w boo-shit! Fuck you not e-e-even! You're the lifetime subscriber to that one!"

They all laughed. Andrew chimed in, "The article will be titled, 'The Lord of His O-Ring: Undercover in jail...*deep* under the covers.'"

More genuine laughter on a Merry fucking Christmas. Funny fucking Indians, these professional jailhouse Indians. The old toothless wino Indian had woke him up that morning for breakfast, shaking him and saying, "Hey! Andrew, wake up! We brought some girls with us. They're nice and ready to pass out—just the way you like 'em!"

He'd almost miss them fuckers, he thought. Almost. He posted bail the next afternoon as planned after giving the old guy his lunch.

The only noteworthy undercover-type story he'd gotten that stuck in his head was when a young 20-year-old sex offender gave a confession of sorts about how he had sex with a 14-year-old runaway. He kept her heavily drugged on pills for days as he phone recorded sex with her several times, according to charges. Well, raped her. It was a 2:30 a.m. conversation and the guy realized he'd be in for a tough time when he got sent to a real prison.

Once, while in a holding cell with another repeat sex offender who was privy to beat downs while in prison, the other perv informed him the trick from being seriously hurt was to stay away from corners and try to remain in the open when attacked. The most severe beat downs came from being trapped in a corner where the hardest kicks and knees could land full force while sometimes the guards couldn't see as other inmates might block the view.

"Shall we practice that theory and beat you in the open tomorrow?" his audience of an old high school classmate asked only half-jokingly. He was rapt and so was Andrew as he pretended to sleep, because what else was there to do to kill time and ignore the real world?

If the sex offender posted bail before trial which was a possibility since his family was rich, he said he was going to go on a mass shooting spree because fuck it, his life was screwed since he'd never be able to find work or have a future. Death by cop suicide would be the outcome, he hoped. His brother had an AR-15. That's what he'd use.

His former classmate and fellow inmate said, "Fuck, knowing my luck I'll come out after serving four months, big ol' cheese-y grin, breathing the first breath of free air and then have it be my last breath— be the first one to get shot right in the lungs in your rampage! Erbz!"

That morning the sex offender requested he be moved because he felt suicidal.

***

The night Andrew went to jail Vicki cried as hard as she'd ever cried. She cried so hard she had to lay her face into a pillow so not to wake her sleeping daughter. She hated that she knew she still deeply loved him. She really didn't want to call the police, but she needed not only her but him to move on and knew that it was the best way to get the message across that it really was over.

He was a potentially colorful flower that simply refused to bloom in spite of her years of nourishment, and now it was winter once again. She needed to forever douse any remaining smoldering embers that might ignite her heart and keep him away awhile. *Ashes! Ashes! We all...fall...down!* But this time she wouldn't let Andrew hold on and grab her to take her down with him. Also, at least his seed that was their daughter would bloom without his darkness covering her sun.

Maybe there was still a future chance for redemption and they could lie together and love and laugh as they used to....

No! He needed to understand she'd be mocked even if she ever did take him back for being weak. It would not only infect her social life in the close-knit tribal community, but perhaps her professional life, too, as people would talk behind her back. Her family and close friends had all by now seen his psychotic texts. Her friends agreed that Andrew probably should not be let around his daughter anymore if he was that supposedly unstable where Vicki actually had to get a restraining order, while her family had mixed-reactions, knowing and realizing the importance of a father in a child's life and knowing at least the guy honestly cared a lot. She needed to stay the strong woman she was, her friends said. It definitely wouldn't be hard to find someone better than Andrew—like her new boyfriend. They said Andrew deserved whatever jail time he got and wasn't a victim because of what he did to her heart as a result of choosing his alcoholism over her. Always remember that mantra.

Vicki knew it was all too far gone now, and he just didn't get it. Maybe now he would. It would be easier for her to hate than to feel any heartbroken or lingering affection. Fuck him, it had to be. There was zero room for him in her life, physically, mentally and especially emotionally. With disdain it was easier to move past him.

From then on, she would simply be too tired to waste tears on him. She'd ran that fountain dry.

***

Outside it grew colder with small flurries of snow in the late afternoon. Andrew only wore a hooded sweatshirt because it was unseasonably warm the day he'd gone to jail. He went to the local tribal college and sat on a sandstone near an outside power outlet smoking a cigarette as his dead phone charged. Up the street and in the alleyway he noticed someone had already thrown out their Christmas tree, its tinsel flickering like festive ghosts of what once was.

He'd avoided alcohol as of late for no real discernible or conscious reason other than he wanted to focus on writing even more. He obsessively and compulsively tweaked a novel he'd written "The End" on about a month prior, and sent in sample chapters to a publishing company. They'd emailed him back just a few days ago, expressing great interest in seeing the rest of his work. If accepted he'd receive a $2,000 advance—enough to buy a decent used vehicle since a chunk of change he'd been saving for that very purpose had just gone to the unjust justice system. Like a protected penguin egg, he kept the novel a closely guarded secret lest fate notice it and be tempted to continue his horrendous streak of foul fortune. Also, a short story of his had been accepted for publication in a local popular book anthology that looked to be a promising jump start to getting his name out there.

The Little Bighorn River was not far. He walked over to the bridge about a hundred yards away that crossed it. He leaned over the railing, staring at the black water below, formulating how he'd go about dealing with everything. He recalled a fictional story he wrote about a young woman writer that almost committed suicide by hanging herself under a bridge on a similar wintry day.

She was so real and piteous to his writer mind. He wondered what ever became of her after that. She was probably writing about Andrew now in a parallel universe writing world, writing about how he'd nearly come to tears every time he saw another daddy with a young daughter. He genuinely chuckled at the depressing notion. He thought of the Little Bighorn Battlefield hill a mile or so away up river. On it there were a few headstones marking where his Cheyenne ancestors had fought so hard and died so Andrew could be in Montana today.

A Cheyenne Warrior fell here on June 25, 1876 while defending the Cheyenne Way of life, the headstones said.

He was a few miles from where his little Cheyenne daughter was. So close, yet so far, as the old adage went. He'd fight for his little one the way his ancestors' had fought for him. His memories conjured a pic of the last time they were together as she painted with watercolors and a dedicated focus. She was such a creative, talented, and sensitive artist, he thought—just like her daddy. He just wished she wouldn't have to be so tough. He imagined the smile on her face if he were allowed to show up, right before she'd run up to give him the biggest hug she could.

A tear fell into the river.

Andrew decided he'd go to the rez border town of Hardin and use the wifi on a motel and edit as much as he could on his phone that night until the sun came up, revising his novel one last time to escape from his reality. He'd stay another night afterward if he had to before sending the manuscript back with his last bastion of remaining hope.

Lately, he dreaded sleep not because of nightmares—quite the opposite, really. He mostly dreamed of a utopian world where he played with his laughing daughter in the park on pleasant days, built snow forts on cold ones, or put puzzles together and painted on rainy ones. But when he woke up, she'd be gone, forcing him to relive the misery of freshly missing her all over again.

He walked back over to the tribal college, touched a button, and his phone came alive as he saw the familiar pixels of Vicki's face. Despite all of it, everything, he instinctively smiled yearningly at it, only wanting to get back together with her.

Like he'd texted earlier that week he was tired of being angry at her, but now the thought he'd legally be banned from seeing his daughter scrambled his emotions violently and had him wanting to hate since he was her protector. He decided love of Vicki was the one thing of his he wouldn't allow her to take, however. He'd love her for being the other precious half of his child. He'd love her just because he always would and was tired of losing people he cared for.

He kissed his phone screen, made a quick prayer that Vicki would forgive him for what he was going to do, and changed the image to his daughter.

Dead Cows and Lies I Was Told
By Dana Lone Hill

On my 18th birthday my adopted parents told me my dad was alive. My *real* dad. I was shocked and almost vomited as my stomach felt like it came up from the floor like I was in an elevator. Why would they do this now?

I already knew I was adopted because it's not easy forgetting the six foster homes I went through before I landed there. My adoptive parents could not have children so they adopted the four of us—all Native boys—although two of my adopted brothers died. So all that was left was me—Mack—and my brother Jake. The two that died were Clarence and Shine.

Our mom and dad were basically nice. They fed us, didn't beat us, and gave us a pleasant ranch home in the Black Hills of South Dakota just outside of Rapid City. Sure, they were really controlling, but it was definitely better than some of the other homes I've been in, and certainly better than bouncing from foster home to foster home and the Juvenile Detention Center. JDC was real scary. I still remember the initial whiff of antiseptic smell, the sounds of shackles dragging on the floor, the continual sound of buzzers and steel doors slamming. I was just ten-years-old the first time I hit that place, and I never wanted to go back again in my life. Unfortunately, it would not the last time I checked in there as I often had to resort to creative means that society frowned upon to help support me and my sisters.

I only looked down at the hard wood floor patterns after they told me my father was alive. Then I pushed my shaggy hair out of the way and looked up. My hand gripped the chair with white knuckles that I was sitting on as I ate my Fruit Loops.

"But...I thought he was dead. What the hell is he? Jesus Christ, now you tell me?!" I said.

"Well, you see we thought...we *heard* he'd died in prison. But I guess it wasn't true, son," my adoptive father told me. He was looking at me with fear in his eyes. Why was he scared? Was he feeling guilty?

"Whatever," I said, got up, and walked out the house slamming the door. I had to get to work and do something to get my mind off of it. I was furious. I had a thousand other things I wanted to scream at the but didn't. My mom's rat terrier followed me, barking happily down the flagstone path.

"Tina, go on." I nudged her with my foot and she acted like I was playing. I pushed her harder and jumped in my old Chevy. My car was older than me but I didn't care. It was legit with insurance even. I'd saved up last summer to buy it from an ad on Craigslist. I set my music in the car to Beastie Boys, "Time to Get Ill," and turned it full blast and lit a cigarette. I had no time to be worrying about my real father or why they were telling me now of all times he was alive.

***

Ever since I went there at age 12, they'd told me he died. But I had a feeling he was in prison because about the time I was hitting JDC, he was going to trial for dealing drugs on the reservation. I remember seeing the article in the Rapid City Journal that a guard was reading and I said excitedly, "Hey, that's my dad!"

The guard looked at it and laughed. "Like loser father, like loser son."

I glared at him and walked away.

Later during a cell raid the same guard slammed me against the wall and roughed me up. He whispered, "So you think you're a tough son of a bitch, huh? Because you know what your dad is? A punk bitch. And where he's going that's all he's gonna be. Same road you're going down...punk bitch."

"Fuck you," I whispered to him.

For two weeks up until my trial date I sat in solitary after he claimed I assaulted him. When I went to trial I was still bruised up from the beating by the guards. That's when they decided to put me in the foster care system. My in and out life of foster care and JDC went on for over two years until I ended up with my current parents Marsha and Jeff. When I was first moved to their house there was a bit of delay because my real mom was still on her death bed, but they hired a judge to rush the paperwork through so I was able to move in before she died. She died from drinking complications, they said. I am not sure of the exact diagnosis.

The last time I'd lived with my mom was when I was 8-years-old. She decided to move all of us to Rapid City. We did fine at first as she worked hard, then she started caring more for meth than she did us. Many times me and my birth sisters ate only what we could find. Melted ice cream soup with crackers, for instance, while my mom sat there with pieces of burnt tin foil around her and a glazed, dull look in her eyes.

On the day the state took us away we'd missed almost two weeks of school. My mom was crashed out hard and we were all eating dry bread. It was the last time I saw my sisters in my life. I always wondered why she left our dad because he made a good life for us on the reservation. But I knew the answer if I was honest with myself: he also had a string of women on the side and our mom always had bruises.

I threw my cigarette out the window and shook the memories from my head. I had no reason to remember my past. I was stronger than that now. I pulled into the employee parking lot at work and looked in the rearview mirror. I had tears in my eyes. I put my thumb on one tear duct and my middle finger on the other. I was trying to plug them up. I didn't need this. Not now. Damn, maybe my dad should have been dead.

I grabbed my employee badge and went to work. Another slow day of slicing Black Forest ham and oven roasted turkey for old folks. I sighed loudly. I hated deli food. I'd been working there all throughout high school and this was the first Fall year since my senior year, but at least I owned my own car and had a good amount of savings to go to college so I wouldn't also have work on the ranch with my brother Jake anymore. With four generations of experienced cattle ranchers, our ranch did well so I didn't *have* to work deli, but I really didn't like stepping in cow shit all day either.

Yet, I still had hadn't applied to any college. I didn't know what I wanted to do or where I wanted to go with my life.

***

I was slicing cheese when my coworker said someone wanted to see me. I looked up and I knew it was *him*. My dad. I held back tears, and swallowed a sob. I mumbled to my supervisor I needed a break. I went out in front of the counter and this old tattooed man bear hugged me. I was crying too hard to look up. I was embarrassed.

"Sh-h-h, Mackie, let's go for a walk." He gently put his arm around me and lead me out the door.

We were in the parking lot and I was still crying like a little bitch. He gave me time and his bandana to blow my snot all over.

Finally, I calmed down a little.

"Happy Birthday," he said.

"You remembered?" I said with an attempt to half-smile.

"Naw," he said. "I never forgot."

"How did you find me?" I asked.

"Facebook said you work here in the deli—slapping meat!" he said and offered me a cigarette. We both laughed.

We were both quiet. Smoking. Puffing. Exhaling.

"Where you staying?" I said.

He reached into his wallet and pulled out a business card for a motel on a street in Rapid known for having seedy motels. He handed me another card with a federal probation officer's number.

"I wrote my room number on one, and the other one has my cell number. That's also my probation officer's number if you ever can't find me. How are your sisters?" He looked at me with a small glimmer of hope.

I looked away. I felt like a failure. I'd lost track of them.

"I don't know. I haven't seen them for 8 years," I said quietly. I thought of them every day. Every...fucking...day—Jennifer and Janay.

"Fuck!" he yelled.

He threw his cigarette on the ground and his hands grabbed his head as I flinched—ready for him to erupt. He'd seen me flinch and tried to calm down. He said, "Sorry, I was just hoping they kept you all together, man."

"Uh, I gotta go back to work." I said. I couldn't shake the need to be with my old family, with him, with my mom, with my sisters. Like...when everything was okay. Usually that was a Saturday morning with sugary bowls of cereal in front of the TV as our mom and dad slept in late. I snapped back to the moment.

He shook my hand hard like a man and hugged me with his other arm.

"If you need anything, call me, okay? *Anything*," he said.

I walked away and thought, *I live in a damn near mansion, he lives in a dive of a motel. What the hell would I need him for?* Deep in my heart I probably knew it wasn't about materialism, however. He knew it as well.

I needed to know who I was.

By that, I didn't mean that I was a deli master, or a good driver, or a smoker, or someone who can draw anyone's eyes really good. I mean,

I can draw more than eyes. I can draw anything. Anything I wanted to. But I wanted to know who I was before I became that kid that was the "burden of the state." Did my dad know?

Fuck it, it was a long time ago, I thought. Fuck that label of "nephew" from drunk aunties and uncles hugging me, smelling like beer and cigarettes. Fuck the label of "my son" by my mom and dad. Where were they when I needed them? I tried forgetting about it as I went back to the deli and finished the last four hours of my shift in a haze.

I slept all those deep thoughts off as soon as I got home, then woke up and smoked two joints to myself on the roof and drank a pint of Crown Royal in my room, chasing it with a Coke. Every once in awhile I staggered through the rest of the house looking for a fight with my adoptive parents or brother. They all smartly steered clear of me. I think the fact that they realized they lied to me—or realized I would have eventually found out they'd lied to me anyway—made them scared and remorseful. As they all retreated to their rooms I stood in the living room and turned the stereo up as loud as I could. Korn's "Alone I Break" was on. I passed out on the couch. Alone, drunk, and in my boxers on my eighteenth birthday, October 2, 2013. It was not until I woke up I realized I never showed up for my sort of surprise party at my sort of white girlfriend's apartment as she and others had texted and called like crazy to come over. Instead, I got drunk and passed out. When I woke up I just laid there stared at the ceiling.

I faintly heard my adoptive parents arguing in their room.

"It was your choice to tell him."

"Yeah, but you made his dad sound like a saint. You made him sound like one of us. As much as we tried and want to make him like us, he *is* just an Indian."

Those were all the words I heard—all the words I needed to hear. I had the day off from work, but I had to leave. Fuck that shit. I put my hoody and jeans on, grabbed my keys and wallet, and left.

As I neared the outer limits of Rapid City the snow was falling hard on October 3rd, 2013. Imagine Dragon's "It's Time" was playing on the radio.

Before I could make it into Rapid, I was pushed off the road by an SUV and spun into the ditch. Panicked, I went quietly out of control into a ditch. The SUV also spun a bit, but only straightened out and continued out of my sight. As my heart steadied, I noticed some of the cows in the ditches, trying gather to seek shelter and heat from each other, but it looked like they were getting stuck to the ground somehow. They were eerily crying and mooing with terrified eyes. I called my house to tell them what happened.

My adopted mom answered. "Mack, can you just call a tow truck? Your dad and Jake went to save the cows! You should have been here helping them and—"

I hung up and called my dad's phone number on the card he gave me.

He asked for directions and said he would be right there as soon as possible.

I waited. After about 20 minutes he showed up driving real slow. He made me help him push my car as far from the road as we could. As we did we actually saw some of the cows in the field just lay down and die in front of us, their stiff legs jutting out as snow drifts piled around them. I turned away from the ghastly sight.

After we jumped in his truck I started to warm up again.

"You going to work?" he said.

I shook my head. "No, I think I was going to see you."

He smiled and turned the Bob Seger song up.

"Cool, cool," he said.

"I feel bad for these cows," I said. "So many people depend on them for a livelihood."

I wasn't just talking about my adopted family but about the many people I'd grown up with in the past eight years. Later, news reports would say tens of thousands of cattle had perished that night during the freak storm—devastating the many local ranching communities.

"Shoot, son, if they lost even a tenth of the 30 to 50 million buffalo they killed so they could starve our people off, they'll be lucky," he said. He whistled. "Still, some storm for this time of year, huh? In a severe storm like this, buffalo always walk right at the direction of where it's coming from. Do you know why?"

Why?" I said, genuinely curious.

"Well, they know that if they go right at the storm and power through it, they'll be able to get through it quicker."

These cattle couldn't go towards the storm. They could only stay behind a fence and be confined there, or if they were lucky they could hide.

He said, "Let's get your car towed, and then you can hang out and learn truth if you want—or you can go back to what they said is your home."

I looked at my dad's hard face, and I knew I was going to go home. I knew home was in my heart. It was in my heart that beat our shared red blood.

Shadows Made by the Weak
Bojan Louis

O tter and I spent the day rolling an abandoned school bus, spray painted pink by a previous occupant, down a hill of loose black cinders and onto the west end of a clearing that bordered his neighbor's property. Otter had brought a chainsaw to cut-to-length a couple of old railroad ties and secured them to the cast iron grill, welded to his truck, using a scavenged combination of nylon rope and bailing wire. We assumed that the pressure of the truck pushing the bus would be absorbed by the oiled oak ties and grill, transferring through the chassis so as to avoid damage to the radiator and 350 engine behind it.

The bus had sat vacant nearly year, gutted of its vinyl green benches and rubberized flooring it accumulated insects and vermin. The tires, though mostly full, were sunk a quarter deep into the soft terrain. In order for me to stay on Otter's property, I'd have to clean the bus, and remodel the interior to make it livable: a seating area with a fold down table for meals, a countertop with cabinets and sink, closet space, and sleeping quarters. Otter offered me this arrangement after a mutual friend put us in touch and we worked a successful landscaping bid together: trench work, PVC, 9 tons of pink granite and river rock, and some damn fountain/pond feature we each pissed in when the job was completed.

Otter sat in his matte black pickup idling and parked behind the bus. We agreed that once Otter revved the engine I was to be ready for the descent. He would ease the truck against the bus, rock it out of the cinders, and down the hill. This was all about momentum. His advice to me was to ride steady, not to turn too sharply at the base so as not to tip before I made the clearing. Even without obstacles the downward pitch didn't appear steep enough to offer much speed. I imagined that the cluster of scrub-juniper at the base might stop the bus short of the clearing.

Otter revved the engine and it reverberated through the empty hull of the bus, a dull hum with loose screws and window casings rattling. The dusty shell creaked as Otter began rocking it with his pickup, each acceleration louder and more urgent than the previous until something buckled and seized. The bus inched forward, crunching the volcanic earth beneath it. The horizon extended before me and the sun reflected off the windshield, which caused large sunspots. As I blinked repeatedly, hoping to regain sight, the bus began to descend the hill like how I imagined roller coasters did, having never ridden one, and the base approached faster than I anticipated. I glanced into the side mirror hoping to see some reflection of comfort, any point from where I'd just been to guide and steer by. Instead, Otter's truck bounced behind. I assumed that the haphazard wood buffer was stuck to the bus' bumper. I turned the steering wheel in the direction of the clearing as smoothly as I could and stomped down on the brake pedal. It fell uselessly to the floorboard. I searched for the emergency brake lever and saw that it had been removed, only the aluminum sign remained in its location. I gripped the steering wheel, cursed my displaced situation, and resigned myself to crash into the tree line.

But the sudden grind and crunch of rock beneath the bus launched me against the windshield. I lay on the floor stunned, my breath knocked out me, while black dust hung in the air.

After I determined that no bones were broken I fought open the folding side door until it collapsed and swung limply ajar by the bottom hinge. Outside dust spun in swirls while the arid, hot air blew over my skin. Beside me the bus was wedged on top of an outcropping of rocks. The front tire was bent inward, the axle snapped.

Crashed into the rear of the bus was Otter's truck, a mess of bent iron, gnarled wood, smoke, and fluids that pooled on the dry terrain. I didn't smell any gas; didn't worry that the vehicle would burst into flames.

Otter was limping down the hill along the tire tracks, looking at them as if they might tell him what went wrong. He was covered in dirt that caked black where it had mixed with the blood on his arms and forehead.

"Should've secured the posts vertically, length-wise," he said. "Didn't think they'd catch on the goddamned bumper."

"You're ride is fucked," I said.

He shaded his eyes, one of which was beginning to swell shut, and spit.

"So it's good I bailed, then. I might be worse off, dead, if I didn't."

He asked me of my condition, which I told him was fine, aside from a headache and some bruises. After some moments considering me then his truck he suggested we hike the mile back to his place, grab tools, welding gear, and attempt to fix his truck by nightfall. With the endorphins we'd released it would be easy, at least as he thought it.

So we trudged up the hill, looked out over the nearly two hundred cinder cones that humped and pointed from the earth. In the far distance, cobalt flats blended into ashen, aqua cliffs, and a horizon-wide mesa collided with the sky. We knew that we underestimated our position, where we wanted to be, and it had us worn.

We gazed down at the damage and Otter said, "It doesn't look all that bad."

***

Otter lived common-law with his woman, Thrush, in a single-story rectangular house that was built on the high ground of a dried up wash and hidden among juniper and cedar trees. It didn't have interior walls so they sectioned off three rooms by hanging sheets and old quilts from the exposed rafters. Aside from the silver lined fiber glass insulation stapled to the ceiling what stood out to me was that their back porch faced east, was without curtains, so as to allow in the first light of morning. Otter told me that he and his wife rose with the sun and generally turned in a couple hours after sundown, which reminded me of my grandma's traditional Navajo way of living; in accordance with the natural cycle of days and seasons, with minimal possessions, with no running water or electricity. Though a large solar panel powered Otter and his wife's place they limited their use of whatever electronics they owned—radio, guitar amp, an 18 volt contractor's pack of power tools, small television and DVD player—and spent their time reading, hemming and repairing, drinking. Otter mostly in regards to the latter.

They had removed themselves from the lackluster college/tourist town life of Flagstaff. Thirty miles away, northeast on Leupp Road, which ran towards the reservation, and nine miles north on Forest Service Road 244. Their "community" was scattered on twenty and forty acre plots. Apocalypse ready and socially misfit: a roofing contractor who shot lemon drops for breakfast and lunch; a woman married to two different men who alternated evenings of domesticity; a man who kept a stray dog army, known to take potshots if you drove too slowly past his property; and Otter and Thrush, too gothic-gypsy for town.

"So you've come out here to straighten yourself out?" Otter asked. "Heard that. I know the consequences of stirring another man's soup. That kind of thing can get you killed or, at the very least, beat down."

He pulled a small, dirtied cooler from beneath a salvaged wooden camp table, which must have been dismantled, rebuilt to fit the room. He laid out sandwich fixings and stood taking inventory of his kitchen; his eye puffed angrily.

"Thrush," he said, "where'd I leave the goddamned whiskey? It isn't in the cabinet."

I made a sandwich while Thrush appeared quietly from the bed-area. She gave me a shy smile and I admired Otter for living with this oddly beautiful woman. She was tall, with long, gangly arms and legs; her breasts and stomach full for her stature. I'd been told she was in the first months of pregnancy, spent her time walking alone or reading in bed. She wore a hand sewn dress with jump boots, dyed her hair black, obvious from the roots in her part and blond underarms.

She noticed Otter's wounded eye immediately, brushed the blue swollen skin with her fingertips, and rested her head on his shoulder. They whispered, in this near embrace, neither showing any sign of closing or widening the distance between them. She pulled back, allowed her palm to drift down and off Otter's chest as she returned to the bed-area—gaze focused away.

Otter exited the front door, reappeared with a dripping wet bottle.

"Had it stashed in the rain barrel to keep it cold," he said. "Works if you leave it overnight and retrieve it first thing, but you'd probably best drink it then." He laughed, as if remembering all the mornings he'd regretted doing just that.

I ate, not wanting to say shit about the tools or welding gear, concerned more with an evening's rest and mend.

***

Afternoon dimmed to dusk as we sat on the back porch facing east, toward the reservation, and sand and limestone cliffs as they became undefined in the falling light.

"Cheating's an inevitability," said Otter. "Listen, someone's bound to know someone cheated on or cheating is all I'm saying. Hell, I've been both."

"You know, I thought I was getting lucky," I said, "getting a girl I went for. But it turned out otherwise."

"People fulfill wants, entertain desires," he said. "And some just want to fall in love, which is something I'll drink to."

He downed his whiskey, poured another, and topped off the glass I'd been nursing. I suspected he wouldn't quit until we'd gone past shit-faced, soiled ourselves in some way, which sounded fine considering the situation. So we raised our glasses, gave cheers to all those in search of love, whether for better or worse, and then again to Otter and Thrush for finding one another despite the circumstances of their getting together.

"She was with a painter, artist kind, not trade," he said. "The moody, self-obsessive type who thought he was the next hot shit. She was lonely, ignored, all that. I'd been hired to rebuild the storage room of the coffee house she worked at, making it bigger. I'd work late, well after she finished closing, so that we could talk. It brightened us up expressing and opening up to one another like that. Well, as it happens, we fucked in the storage room when it was complete. But she felt guilty, stopped talking to me, and continued to go around with that painter all sullen and quiet as before. This was back in Louisiana."

After that Otter verged on drowning out his life completely when the painter and Thrush decided to move to Seattle, the scene supposedly more fit for the guy's art. Otter, unable to bear the thought of never seeing Thrush again, drove straight through to Seattle, pissing in cups, eating bread loaves, and dissolving Benzedrine in coffee. When he reached her doorstep, he declared his love while the impotent canvas-cuddler stood by, meek and quiet. Otter and Thrush ended up out here after they found forty acres for forty thousand, he told me.

We returned indoors after nothing more could be said and cleared the table of strewn sandwich parts, felt our way to the front door in the darkness, Thrush having turned in sometime well before. Otter insisted that he accompany me to the bus, if only to kill the bottle. We walked without talking. Otter staggered freely on the soft ground and raised the bottle to his mouth mechanically. The night was cool—invigorated, new in its unfamiliar silence and darkness.

Once we reached the clearing, Otter pulled a small flashlight from his pocket, shined it on the crashed vehicles; shadows made by the weak beam made them look more violently abandoned.

"Since you plan on staying awhile you're going to need a place to shit first. Can't just keep digging random holes and burying it," he said. "Outhouse. You'll need to dig a pit, build an outhouse."

"Makes sense," I said. "Used to use one at my grandma's old hogan. I'm not above using them."

"Then you know what I'm talking about," said Otter. "Come around the house in the morning. I'll set out whatever tools you need and material as well. It'll be a good way for you to settle in out here and give me, us, time to get materials for the interior work."

Otter pointed the light ahead of the bus, moved it side to side.

"Build the outhouse over there by those trees. Here, I'll mark it for you."

He stumbled to the spot, struggled with his pants while not letting go of the bottle, and pissed, first in his pants, then in spurts until he was finally able to get his dick free of his fly. Walking back toward me he cussed, took a long pull, and retched but held it down.

"I don't sleep clothed anyhow," he said. "See you in the morning."

He wavered past me back into the mess of trees, a waft of urine and booze.

***

To leave shit piled, exposed, signifies sloth and inability. A dog will bury its shit; paw dirt over its piss. Cats use boxes, have been rumored to operate toilets, lowering their asses and defecating, even wiping and flushing. This basic courtesy for the owner can be learned early and, with diligent tutoring, quickly. Humans, however, require a period of soiling themselves during the beginning and end of their lives that necessitates a changing, which otherwise puts our health and social grace at risk. Our potty training takes years, if only because all the sitting, wiping, and washing undermine the ways in which we prefer to spend our time. And once we learn to appreciate plumbing and the toilet it's the fact that we shit that we attempt to hide.

Sometime after mid-day—having made three trips for tools and material with only the sheeting left to get—I'd dug a ten-foot deep hole, three-feet in diameter, which made the work difficult. I used a bucket attached to the end of a rope attached to a juniper and removed the earth and rocks by climbing the rope, then hefting up the dirt filled bucket. On what was supposed to be the final load I dropped back into the hole, both exhausted and hungry, without thought to the bucket or rope. The many attempts I'd made to scamper and claw my way up had spent me of all my energy—my fingertips and hands raw. Shouting had also done nothing, so I sat with my knees pulled against my chest like some incapable fetus and waited. I knew that it was inevitable for Otter to come down and check on me once evening approached.

A breeze swirled dust down onto me and the sun began its slow slide off the sky.

I dozed on and off for an unknown number of hours; stood when I heard the crunch of footsteps approaching.

"Down here. I'm in the fucking hole. Down here."

It was Thrush who peered over the edge, a shadow of drooping hair.

"What are you doing down there?" she asked. "That's where the shit goes."

"Well, I did too good a job clearing out the base and forgot the rope to climb out with. Got my shovel though."

She nodded and I noticed her smile; pale teeth accentuated by her shadowed face.

"I don't know that I'll be able to pull you out by the shovel," she said.

"You can throw the rope down. I've rested long enough to climb out of here."

"Right. You want the bucket, too?"

"Rope's fine," I said.

As I climbed out, Thrush helped by yanking my shirt, then the waist of my jeans so that I landed on my chest.

"How long have you been down there like that?" She laughed, tried covering it with her hand but laughed harder. "I'm sorry, this is sort of ridiculous."

"Fuck, two hours at least, probably three. Long enough to know I'm starved."

She was in stitches, held her side, said, "Jesus, I never laugh this much."

"Then get in all you can."

She patted the dirt from my clothes. The warmth of her hands caused me to tell her that I was cold. She licked her thumb, rubbed dirt splotches around my eyes gently, and instead of matching her gaze, I walked to my water jug. I choked as I swallowed, which made me more aware of my hunger, and I wanted her close again.

"We're making dinner up there," she said. "That's why I came down. Otter's busy with the fire. He hitched a ride to town earlier for food and whatever. Let's go, I'm sure you haven't prepared anything for dinner."

I grabbed a hoodie from the bus and we began our walk to the house.

Thrush's pace was slow, hesitant, as if she wanted to tell me something but moved ahead drawn by doubt. We navigated the faint path by the glow of the moon and horizon, which was a thin line of orange and sapphire. She stopped suddenly and I nearly collided with her. I inhaled the musky, patchouli scent of her hair. She reached into her skirt pocket, pulled out a pouch of roll-your-owns, and faced me, her eyebrows raised.

"Yeah, sure," I said.

She rolled a cigarette, handed it to me, and rolled one for herself. She lit hers first, offered me the flame. I leaned in, cupped it against the breeze, and tried not to touch her hands but my hunger from not eating all day caused me to waver. She gripped one of my hands and I drew in the flame.

"You know," she said, "that story Otter told of him and I ending up together, didn't happen exactly like he told it."

"You were listening in on all that?" I asked.

She shrugged and we continued on to the house, slow as before.

"Let me guess," I said. "He never drove all that way?"

"No, he drove the whole way. But he didn't just arrive to my door and sweep me off my feet. He lived in his truck for nearly six months doing odd jobs for money. It wasn't until Howie kept disappearing and our apartment slowly emptied and the tracks on Howie's arm led from one to the other, and between his fingers, that I'd even talk to Otter."

She stared into the dusk, took a long drag.

"Sometimes your first choice isn't the one that works out. Women work with their hearts, when we've loved someone, we always do, at least a little. Even when they're out of our lives we care about them, hope that they'll take care of themselves. It's always that first choice, that first love that's hardest to get furthest from."

Evening shadows and the ember of her cigarette made her face appear gaunt. She was tired—I could see that—not from anything that day or the ones before it, but from those facts recounted over and over in her head.

"So you don't love Otter like you loved Howie? That isn't something shocking or to feel guilty about, I guess? I don't think that I've ever been in love like that to tell you the truth."

She nodded as if she'd anticipated this answer. I was in my early twenties, male, hardworking, with no resolve to maintain a relationship, or so I imagined myself. Otter and Thrush were easily ten years older than I was, with more experience and knowledge of intimacy, relationships, and heartbreak.

"So that's not what landed you way out here in the middle of nowhere with a couple you hardly know?" she asked. "From what little I've been told and understand it was a girl or the failed situation with a girl that brought you out here."

I admitted that was the case. Foolish attraction, a rehab stint, and the thought or misconstrued belief that my efforts, no matter how dire or genuine, assured me the chance to a lasting relationship with a girl I knew little about. The moments we shared, I realized, should have sufficed.

"You're learning," Thrush said. "You've got to know that a lot of couples are unhappy and possibly stuck for whatever reasons that are beyond their control. Take me for example, stuck out here with Otter, and eventually this baby. It's important to take chances, to know when and how to take them, or else you'll live a life regretting the opportunities that you didn't take."

She took another long drag on her cigarette and commented on how she'd soon have to give them up, and dropped it on the cinders, then grounded it out beneath her shoe.

"Well," I said, filled with uncertainty and doubt, "I don't know if that's any of my business."

"I just wanted to tell you," she said.

She smiled like she did when she peered down at me from the top of the outhouse hole and walked on ahead without hurrying, so that it didn't look as if she was trying to get away.

When we reached the path that led to the front of the house, Thrush let me enter the house first. No one was inside, though a few candles were lit. Smoke drifted in through the sliding door, creating a horror movie ambiance. Thrush grabbed cups from the cabinet, gave me one without a glance, and led the way out back.

Outside, Otter stood before a fire, used an unlit cigarette to make slight stabbing motions as he talked to himself, or the fire—of which I wasn't sure, and didn't care to know.

When he saw us, he said, "The grill's ready, you'd better be hungry. Where've you been all damn day? Are you that slow digging a hole?"

"No, I'm just sore from yesterday." I looked at Thrush, who grinned.

"He jumped in the hole without a rope," she said.

Otter doubled over laughing, nearly stumbled into the fire but leapt over to the side. He was drunk already. He called me a stupid shit, asked if I'd ever in my life dug a hole over my head. I hadn't, so I shrugged.

"I've fallen off most everything that I've worked on," said Otter. "But I've never dug myself into a hole I couldn't get myself out of, never known anyone who has."

Here, we all laughed, so much that we held our guts. It was funny— pure accident. The only person who could be held accountable was me, for forgetting one simple thing: let in my way out.

***

The next morning, I woke beside a smoldering pile of ash and wood ember, its warmth a vague reminder of a body pressed close to mine the previous night. I grabbed at the ground around me, found nothing, sat up, rubbed my eyes, and focused on the evidence that remained. Bone-clean pork chops and oddly shaped aluminum foil, half-packed with potatoes were strewn about. Two empty bottles placed suspect on the bench. The rear sliding door to the house shut.

A scattered recollection returned to me of Otter and Thrush quitting the evening after a pointless conversation about relationships and happiness. His viewpoint was that someone either walked with you, saw things your way, or they walked alone; hers that a compromise was made, otherwise, one just dragged the other along. He'd attempted to kiss her but she pushed him away, told him he was horrible at it, drunk as he was, and that he needed to be put to bed. That memory blackened, fluttered to a time later—me, sitting and smoking, retired to inner solitude, unfed flames shrinking—an emptiness widening within me. In the broken moment, Thrush returned quietly, sat beside me on the bench. Neither of us spoke. What seemed like moments or hours later I wandered away to piss behind some trees. After I finished and turned around, Thrush was there, standing beyond the throw of firelight, her hands clasped as if prepared to deliver some unfortunate news. She advanced, grabbed my forearm, and pressed against me, her lips warm and wet on my neck. I held her awkwardly in response, not tightly or with any urgency, but firm enough to let her know that I wouldn't let go first. She told me that everything was all right, Otter was passed out. I said something about being too shitty, probably couldn't get it up. She sighed, disappointed or angry perhaps with the wasted effort. We released each other and she led me back to the bench, laid me down, and all went black again.

The morning was crisp and I pissed, weighed with uncertain guilt, on the coals to douse anything that would burn. As I tucked myself away, I felt a heavy, backed-up pain in my balls, which meant that Thrush and I may have tried to initiate something physical and only gotten so far, or that one of us maybe got to where we wanted. I hoped for Thrush's benefit rather than mine and focused on the taste of my dried mouth—nothing musky or uncertain.

Behind the two whiskey bottles on the bench I found a pouch of tobacco—Thrush's I imagined—and rolled two smokes, leaving the pouch. I walked to the rear sliding door, peeked in, didn't discern any movement, and headed around to the front of the house. I grabbed a cut of sheeting and made my way down the path carrying it at an angle above my head, alternated the arms that bore the weight until I had to drag it. I made a mental note to butt the dragged, damaged edge against the peak of the roof on the backside of the outhouse, where it'd be unseen.

By the time I reached the bus the morning dew had evaporated and birds like miniature bells signaled a new day's heat. I rinsed my face, wiped my body with a damp rag. I wanted to feel fresh before another day's sweat. With the hole dug and ready, I grabbed some two-by-eights, hand-sawed them to length, and nailed them into a box frame, squaring each corner. Next I framed-out the floor joists and shitter hole. While I measured and marked out studs, I heard footsteps on the cinders—my heart raced. I wanted it to be Thrush but knew it wasn't.

Otter stood with a hammer in one hand, a steaming mug in the other. His eye swelled to a blackened fist; his face large, exaggerated, primal.

"Did ourselves in last night," he said. "Wasn't for the food one of us might have ended up in the fire."

"The night's a blur to me," I said.

"Who're you telling? I was sure Thrush and I went to bed together, but I have this faint notion she crawled back in later during the night. I can't be certain though."

"Maybe she had to pee," I said.

"That's probably what it was. Anyway, I came down to lend a hand, make sure you don't end up back in that hole again."

I nodded, thanked him for his help, and we got to work measuring, cutting, and nailing. During this time, he told me that Otter wasn't his real, given name—I'd guessed as much—but something he used to tag in Louisiana, then in Flagstaff. It was a fast tag—four sprays with a can, four scribbles with a marker. He drew it out for me in pencil on a two-by-four. An O connected to two lower case *t*s then to an R; the E incorporated with three horizontal lines across the top, through the center, and along the bottom. As much as he said he tagged it, I'd never seen any graffiti resembling it anywhere. Maybe he wanted me to know that whatever I came to learn about him, whatever he chose to share, was temporary—flux.

He scribbled out the tag and we used the piece for one of the top plates.

Later, as we worked with a cut of sheeting, Thrush arrived with a plastic container and thermos. She appeared happier than the day before, walked lighter, and smiled at me before looking at Otter.

"Who told you to bring food?" he asked.

Her smile fell flat, stern. "No one needs to tell me to do anything."

This tension made me think to say that I wanted something to eat, but quickly realized the food was brought in consideration of me, and that I was the tension. I stood silent, kept my eyes on Thrush.

"You don't have to eat it, Otter," she said. "Who said it was for you anyway?"

"Oh, so now that we have a guest you'll do something other than lay around in bed with books all day? Maybe you'll have a drink? Or maybe you'll sleep the whole night where you're supposed to?"

Thrush dropped the container and thermos; she slouched saddened, hurt. "I'm pregnant, Otter. Why the fuck would I have a drink? And what do you care that I stay in bed? You fumble your way in every night shitfaced and useless, smelling like a distillery. Maybe I want to sit and chat, too?"

Otter waved it off and silence rose from the ground beneath us. A dust-devil spun up, died, and I backed away.

"I think you two need a minute," I said.

Thrush stared at the ground, swallowed down some emotion or comment.

Otter faced me, a sickness come to his unhurt eye. He rushed me and Thrush screamed something inaudible. I relaxed, set my legs for the impact, and dropped my hammer as his fist connected with my face.

I gave him that one, so that he'd at least feel that he'd taken something back from me. I'd not seek his forgiveness, his wife, or play father to his expected child. We'd survive this and only burden Thrush.

On the ground, in the clearing, we breathed dust, swallowed cinders, and released one another's blood knowing that at some point there'd be a resolution, and then there wouldn't be.

***

The outhouse was never built, the bus never remodeled, at least by me. After the fight, which left both Otter and I with bruises, busted lips and noses, and gashed knuckles he told me that I was no longer welcome, which was obvious. He needed to say it in order to put an end to any further fighting or aggravation. I nodded and mumbled while holding my shirt to my bleeding nose that I'd be on my way as soon as I gathered up my belongings. I'd initially ridden out with Otter in order to assure that I'd wouldn't turn tail and haul ass back to Flagstaff if I got bored or frustrated. In that moment, however, each wound hot and pulsing, I regretted taking the uncertain kindness of strangers.

On the walk out of the community of twenty and forty acre plots Thrush yelled from behind me to hold up. I was about a mile past her and Otter's place with eight more to go before I hit the main road. She was winded from the effort of catching up to me and held a gallon water jug.

"Thought you could use extra," she said, "it's a long hike out. Doug's pissed and a fourth of the way through a bottle anyway."

I nodded and scanned the dirt road and terrain ahead of me hoping to see the rising dust of an approaching vehicle. But the air was still and empty.

"If the truck was working I'd drive you out. But, I'm sure it'll be a few more days before Doug can get himself together to fix it."

"Doug," I said. "That's his name."

"Doug. Otter. It really doesn't matter. He's still just an asshole."

"So, then, why do you stay?" I asked.

She shook her head, as if to say that I wouldn't completely understand.

"I do *love* him," she said. "But I don't foresee it getting better between us. After I have this baby and I can travel, I've got friends far from here who I can stay with. It's best for the both of us. Doug is no father. I know that now. Besides, he'll be fine. He's charming and can convince the pants off most any girl he wants to."

Thrush handed me the extra water jug and I thanked her. She moved to hug me, kissed my swollen lips, and told me that she hoped I made it back to town safely. I thanked her again for the water and made an attempt to say something more, perhaps that if she wanted, she could stay with me in town or that there might be a better situation for her than staying with Otter until the baby was born. But knowing that I didn't know what any of this meant Thrush put a hand to my mouth, blew me a kiss, and told me to get moving. If I started at a steady pace then someone would surely be on the way to town, or at least to the main road, and I could save myself the exhaustion and possibility of being stranded for the night on roads where I might otherwise be seen as a vagrant or apparition.

Blood Sport
By Sterling HolyWhiteMountain

I'll cut your throat you white motherfucker.
~William S. Burroughs

1

When the boy was born he did not have enough blood. His name was Lawrence. His parents thought about this fact often, their son not having the necessary blood to be an enrolled tribal member. Early on they would talk about this, and then later on, when he was around three or five, they had largely stopped talking about it, accepting his status as an unenrolled indian the way farmers might accept drought, or soldiers might accept their pending death certificates. He was their son. He was a Blackfeet. Even if his tribe would not accept him, his parents would raise him to know what he was. Then dad died in a driving accident, and mom kind of lost it, and left the kid with her parents, and did not come back.

When the girl was born she had enough blood. Her name was Kim. The girl's parents had a different time with it, the issue of blood. Dad, outside of the fact that he knew his daughter was an enrolled tribal member, never thought about what her blood quantum numbers were. If you were to ask him to this day he would not be able to tell you her exact fraction. The numbers didn't matter. She was enrolled. The mother, though, thought about it often as the girl started to grow up, particularly after she had her first period, waking up to sheets stained with blood. She told her daughter, My girl, you can date a boy if he is not enrolled, but you can never have a kid with one. Do you understand? she said. The girl nodded her head. That's why it's best to just stay away from them.

Kim had light ochre skin and brown hair like her mother. Her dad, on the other hand, was dark-complected, and in the summer when he was out putting up or renovating structures owned by the tribe, and later on overseeing such projects, he got so dark his skin took on a purple hue. When Kim was four she wanted to jingle dress dance but mom wouldn't let her. She said she didn't want her daughter to be one of those dirty kids running around at a powwow. And she didn't want to see her girl all sunburnt, either, because that would remind her of when she got sunburned as a girl, and her darker friends would call her a white girl. The memories of crying in front of her friends sometimes still hung about her like clouds around a mountain, and she did not want her girl to have to think about crying in front of her friends, or remember how her friends would treat her after.

When Kim got older she showed signs of someday being beautiful, and her mom would keep her close at basketball games. Once when she got up to use the restroom at halftime she came back to find two boys sitting next to Kim, both of them leaning in toward her. She asked them who their people were, and after getting an answer she told them they needed to go. That night she called her sister to find out what her sister knew about the boys' families—her sister was one of those one-woman reservation news stations—and the next day she called her cousin who worked in the enrollment office to see whether or not either boy was a real tribal member. One was, the other was not. She told Kim she could only be friends with those boys because she was related to both of them. In truth the girl was related to only one of the boys—the enrolled one—but not the other. But mom wanted to keep things simple.

Then she was in high school. Bigger lockers, assemblies with hundreds of other students, her new girlfriends, boys. The attention of a few senior boys, the way they would look at her and were so confident.

The world slowly opening up to something larger, more full, her first boyfriend, Bobby Last Rider, a kid from Bear Head her mother never knew about because it hardly went anywhere or lasted, they would hold hands and kiss sometimes and he would try to get her to come to his house with him after school, his parents were gone, he held her by the wrist, almost pleading, she felt a pull in her chest like he had hooked a chain to her ribs and was pulling, pulling hard enough that there were moments she didn't see straight, she felt surrounded by him. But she never went, her mom came to get her every day, waiting out there in the blue Dodge dually with strands of hay scattered in its bed, she would go to her because she knew if she didn't her mom would come looking for her, and then she would see them, and then it would be over for sure. Then later Frank Sailor, a light-complected kid with the prettiest green Cree eyes, he was a transfer from North Dakota, his mom worked at IHS, his dad was a school administrator, he was the first skater she had ever seen, with his Vann's and his band t-shirts and walking with his skateboard down the halls even though he couldn't ride it to school because the streets and sidewalks around LaFleur were jacked, and because there was gravel scattered everywhere. He was the first guy she touched who had a tattoo—an eagle head on his left forearm—and she remembered the first time he put his hand between her legs, when they were alone in English hall during a Friday night basketball game, she had been sitting in the pep club section, and she had simply stood up and walked out of the gym and into the back halls with her mom watching, knowing her mom was following her with her eyes, knowing there would likely be repercussions, but Frank had been sitting next to her, and she had decided he wanted him to touch her, and so she had told him to come with her. She looked down and there was his tattoo, something she would laugh about later. The next day her mom took her to IHS and she got her first birth control prescription. A year later, after Frank broke up with her because she wouldn't let him get her panties off, she lost her virginity to me, and a month after that she started dating Dale Nobody's Gun, and that went for three years until they broke up before she headed for Cali.

There were other things to school, of course, honor roll was easy enough, her male teachers loved her both because she knew how to be the sweetheart they wanted, and let's be honest, because she was pretty, and with the women who taught her she found ways into their sympathies by acting the daughter to their authority. She ran track well, hurdles and high jump, and more than one male track coach from opposing teams commented on her long legs, and how much they would like to get some of that for themselves, and studs from other track teams would come over to talk to her, or run warm ups with her, smiling like jackals the whole time. (There was another girl on the team who was prettier than Kim, but she was not what white America wants —her ass was flatter than Kim's, her tits smaller, her teeth were a little crooked, her black hair hung in a long ponytail, swishing back and forth while she ran the 400 and the 800, her strides longer and easier than Kim's, her smile the sweetest shyest thing I ever saw, she was quiet and modest the way those raised by their grandparents are, she turned me down the summer after she graduated by never getting back to me.) There was the LaFleur Academic Bowl team, Kim the traveling alternate her junior and senior years, she probably could have been on the starting four but she didn't feel like putting that kind of effort in, and besides there were so many girls at school who were already jealous bitches toward her, she didn't need to feed them even more ammunition, but she did like to go on trips, she loved going from person to person on the bus to talk with them to find out whatever she could about what was going on lately. So alternate worked. And basketball all four years, although by her senior year she largely rode the bench unless there was a blowout, in which case she came in and played hard and passed up open outside shots and boxed out like a badass. She was a good defender, too, but she was one of those players who knew her own limitations too well, she knew when she was overmatched, and that affected her play, unlike Katie Earrings, who might have been a lesser athlete than Kim, but she also had that strange capacity to delude herself into believing she was better than she was, which actually made her better than she was, and she felt the need to point out sometimes to Kim that she was the better player, At least I don't have splinters in my ass, she would say sometimes if she and Kim got into it, to which Kim would respond with, in her head, and one time out loud, which pretty much cut whatever tenuous threads of friendship there were between them, At least I'm not a black ugly whore like you.

Here are a few of the things Kim got Lawrence did not get because she had enough blood and he did not have enough blood: a federal check issued the start of each December as a result of a 1962 Indian Claims Court settlement for a massive 1877 land theft on the part of the US that reduced our reservation by eighty-percent while we were just beginning to starve—the check usually somewhere between twenty-five and fifty dollars distributed to each enrolled member on and off the reservation, just enough to pay for one-eighth of a pair of shoes, checks that have since stopped coming because while land and water is forever, federal money is for twenty years or so; four years of JOM checks in high school that were given out to enrolled tribal members, the secretary's voice blaring out over the school intercom saying the JOM checks are ready would enrolled members please come get their checks would all *enrolled members* please come get their checks, me and Kim and all the other kids with enough blood leaving in the middle of class to get our money while the kids without enough blood stayed at their desks; hundred dollars her sophomore and junior years for each player on varsity basketball who had enough blood before they headed to the state tourney, which included her as an alternate the first year and as a bench player the second year—this money was given by the tribal council, which is the governmental body that oversees most political and legal doings on the reservation, in whose bi-annual elections you can participate if you have enough blood. There were also Kim's appearances in the local paper, which was more often than most because she was involved in so many different extracurricular activities, and each time she was listed an enrolled member of the Blackfeet Tribe. Which no one really thought about unless, say, you were born without enough blood, like Lawrence, who won grassdance champion at the winter powwow in seventh grade (even then he was fucking beautiful, the kind of dancer who held you in one spot like a fast approaching storm) was mistakenly listed in the weekly paper as an enrolled tribal member along with the other top two who placed. His grandpa had sat him down and explained very carefully that he was not enrolled and why he was not enrolled and what it meant that he was not enrolled. He told him this is how it would be for him, and that while he probably did not understand what it meant he would someday. He said this thing was going to follow Lawrence around like a dog but that dogs weren't so bad if you knew when to kick them and when to feed them. (Lawrence never did understand what he meant, but he heard those words for the rest of his life, the rich timbre of his voice, the kindness beyond kindness the man held for those he loved.) But you're an indian, the old man said, and touched Lawrence on the chest where his heart was. That was the beginning of knowing himself as something separate from the rest. He would come to see he could not think of himself without seeing himself as separate, the same way he knew the sky was blue, or that cowboys always win.

In addition to not getting any of the aforementioned things Kim got (all of which can be spoken of the same way one speaks of the benefits received because you belong to a country club, or the Mickey Mouse Club) he got the following: lousy comments from people who didn't like him or from friends who felt like letting him know his place in the playground hierarchy: Fuck you ain't indin. Or, Fuck this guy is just a white boy. Or, Fuck this one, don't cut yourself you might lose your color. —this last comment not making all that much sense, given that he had darker skin than some of the kids who were teasing him, but it was the playground so who's counting, the playground is about king of the mountain, not fairness or logic or the consequences of contemporary indigenous people internalizing colonial perspectives imported from an island off the northwest coast of Europe centuries before there was asphalt or backboards or bent rims or outdoor basketballs used so often their surfaces so slick the ball slid smoothly under your fingertips when you drove to the hoop. The feeling was beautiful, the feeling erased every other feeling, the feeling erased your self and all the history that made you. There were also the times he was cruising with his friends or cousins, riding shotgun or at one of the back seat doors but never in the middle because fuck that noise—sometimes I was with them, even though I was four years out of high school already and my face had taken on that bitterness familiar to anyone who has really lived in indian country—cruising before ball practice and someone would just start talking ish about someone saying fuckers like that weren't even indin and you could tell they didn't have the blood because they were light-complected, or they would talk about Tony Yellow Old Man, who didn't just have light skin but blonde hair and blue eyes too, and they would rip on him for a while, Fucker is just a white boy posing as a indin, and, Guys who look like that shouldn't be allowed to have indin names, and, If he weren't a such a good ball handler we could just kill him. And then: Fuck hey you should kill him anyway after the way he dunked on you the other day. And everyone laughed, including Lawrence, because it was such a rugged thing to say, but also the dunk had been a poster-shot type dunk, with Tony's crotch smashed into the guy's face. One time Lawrence had said fuck he wasn't enrolled, said it just to see what the guys would say. His girl has just left him for another guy, and he wasn't having any of it. Martin Calf Gun swore and asked was he serious, real loud because he had been driving around repeating things his mom was saying about people who weren't enrolled, how all the breeds should be floated off the reservation, things like that. I said they should all be lined up and shot because that would be faster. Put the fuckers out on a ridge, I said, the way the white man put out our dead after starvation winter. People talked for a minute or three trying to figure out how Law was not enrolled but still be as dark as he was. Someone asked how he could have two enrolled parents but not be enrolled. I said it was further proof that indians are bad at math. Jokes about how he needed to cut his braids off. Jokes about how much time he spent at the tanning salon. I didn't say anything because I had known all along about him, because my mom was like Martin's mom, and Law's grandpa was the guy trying open the flood gates, as my mom was fond of saying, to the people who weren't really indian because they did not have enough blood. Martin solved the conundrum when he stated that Law was one of the good ones so he would be allowed to live. This other guy said at least Law wasn't part nigger like Joe Kills Last. Everyone laughed. Other things he heard when people discovered he did not have enough blood: But you should be, you're dark enough. And, Fuck this guy, you never told me you was white, followed by, Naw jokes, you ain't white, but you're still a faggot. And, Ain't my fault your great-grandma liked fuckin white guys.

After they graduated the three of us went to college. Law went to Silver Falls, staying in-state because he wanted to walk on to the team. Every indian in Montana along with a few white people who understood the beauty and greatness of indian ball said he should've gone full-ride to one of the bigger schools, maybe even out of state, because he was that sweet with a ball in his hands, he had all the stats and all the big game shots and the old fearless on-court poetics gifted only to indian ball players. But we also knew nobody in Montana was taking an indian guy on full-ride after how bad Steve Bad Horse Thief from over Ft. Peck way fucked up during his tenure at U at Riverside, dropping out of school his third year because of a DWI and going home and then getting fucked up on meth, even though the team made it publicly known they wanted him back. But then what would you do if there had been three white kids all teammates who got stopped the same night, across town after leaving the same party you left, and only you got the door prize? Lawyers plus local media make up a miraculous evil in this world. But too Law was the first member of his immediate family to go to college or university, so going to one of the handful of smaller out-of-state schools that recruited him would have been as alien to him as declaring Jesus Christ as the savior of the Blackfeet Nation after a few times attending sweats with his grandpa. Kim went to a high-end California school because she had those flawless grades and that salutatorian plaque and those outstanding test scores and because her mother had made her apply to such schools, sitting her down to go through applications with her, saying no daughter of hers was gonna hang around this place and get knocked up by some reservation fuck up. As for me, I decided to finish my degrees at the local CC, because why the fuck not, I'd had enough of hanging out doing nothing and getting high with my high school cousins, maybe it was time for me to stop fucking around. Plus I had been out there, I didn't feel like turning into a white guy the way I'd seen my older brother turn into a white guy, only coming home for Christmas, telling me and my mom we needed to get out of here (the way he had), we needed to see how big the world was so we could see how small this place was (the way he did), The people here are fucked up, he would say, It's never gonna get better, he would say, you guys should just come stay with me in Tacoma, he would say. But also if I was honest, I didn't know what I wanted. Sometimes the truth is that simple, and that is exactly why you cannot admit it to yourself.

I can see now that college molded Kim and Lawrence into a particular type of American Indian, a forceful and violent shaping from which neither would ever quite recover. Kim, with her light brown skin and light brown hair but clearly non-caucasian features settled into a kind of stunning, alien beauty—at least outside of indian country. When in places where the only indian people anyone knew of were likely the men who spent their lives committed to militarily resisting the tidal wave of American immigrants flooding illegally into their respective territories, the men who either died fighting American colonists or lived long enough to be killed treacherously by one of their own after being forcefully confined to a reservation, the men who by now were just cool native guys in cool memes on various social media platforms to whom cool phrases were attributed regardless of the truth of such attribution —in these places (most of America) Kim was an exotic animal somehow released from her cage. Whereas in indian country everyone recognized her, because indian people by the time they are adults have developed a special radar in order to detect others like themselves, the radar a survival skill akin to changing your colors to blend into environmental surroundings, or moving through the world without leaving behind a trace, the kind of skills developed when exposed over long periods of time to a largely hostile environment. And in that way she was still beautiful, but she was not particularly special, she was an indian among indians, she did not feel like she was being singled out by men because she was the first flower of her kind they had seen. But out in that other world of northern California...there she found herself literally pursued by any number of men, all of whom hailed from different parts of the world, all of whom seemed to want something from her that had nothing to do with her. Not long after she had first arrived she had found a route she enjoyed running, one shaded by the trees that edged the river, then arced through the center of campus, and looped around to finish at her dorm doorstep. More than once while she was running alongside a road or street listening to her headphones (usually top-40 pop, or 70s rock, a gesture of affinity toward her reservation childhood where that decade would seemingly live forever in more ways than one) she noticed a man suddenly running next to her, waving his hand to get her attention, and she would slow down, then stop, and take off her headphones, only to hear the man telling her how beautiful she was, and could he take her to dinner, or out for a drink, could he at least know her name, maybe her number, etc. The first time this happened she was flattered, said yes, she wasn't sure what else to do, spent the night feeling larger than her origins, and things went as far the man kissing her after dinner and then calling the next morning to tell her he was in love with her. After a month or so of this she decided to change her run route, a decision she regretted because of how pretty the run had been, she had loved seeing the water while she ran, but a necessary one nonetheless. Then she changed her route again. And again. Eventually she developed a long term plan for her runs, one in which she regularly switched her route, and was always on the lookout for new possibilities, one in which she sometimes ran on the treadmills at different gyms on campus, and several times she took up free temporary gym memberships around the city, stopping when it was time to pay in order to continue. There were other common instances: guys catching up to her while she walked across campus, guys sitting next to her in the cafeteria, guys sitting down across from her while she tried to study, guys sitting next to her in class and trying to talk to her while she took notes, guys practically assaulting her on various social media platforms, etc. The non-indian men loved her, and each of them regardless of where he was from, once he figures out what she was, wanted to know how much she was. Even the German exchange student, who she only made it through half a date with, and who she only went out with because he was taller than her, and she was tired of going out with guys shorter than her, asked how much indian blood she had. Did she dance? There was something different about her. Despite her irritation with the relentless attention she was changed, the way a prisoner slowly but surely comes to fit the shape of her cell. She began to recognize herself as a commodity with some kind of value she didn't quite understand. At least among the non-indian men she seemed to be such. Among the indian men she met, most of whom were urban, and most of whom preferred the term *native*, the men she met through the indigenous language club, and the committee that put together the yearly powwow, these guys had very little to do with her. They had no difficulty being friends with her, they had intellectual conversation, they felt a kind of solidarity in relation to larger political trends affecting indian people—but they had a strong preference for her girlfriends with darker skin, with black hair, with the look that everyone, indian or white or otherwise, seemed to be looking for when they went out hunting for the often sought but rarely acquired indian princess. One night at a largely all native party one of these guys, this Navajo who seemed draped in turquoise and black leather and had the skin of a god, who had grown up in Santa Fe and had done some modeling (had she seen he was featured in a spread in last month's issue of Cowboys & Indians), he was visiting from an Ivy back east (had she ever been to an Ivy), not to mention he called himself a writer every chance he got (had she seen any of his articles regarding such and such issues in Pine Ridge), who carried himself without the humility so often displayed by men on our reservation, this guy had the gall to tell her that the two of them should hook up. He could never be with her because he couldn't risk his kids turning out as light as her, but they could have fun while he was visiting if she was into that. She should give him her number so he could send her some pics, she would be impressed, he did ab workouts every morning for an hour. For her part Kim thought he smoked like one of the beautiful celluloid white women she had seen smoking cigarettes held in cigarette holders in her Early

American Cinema class.

There were also the women who cut her hair—after only a few trips to the salon she began to dread those conversations. Because what else did you do, cutting a woman's hair, but ask her about herself? She came to appreciate selfishness in a cosmetologist; those hour-long sessions once every few months were the only time she wanted to be in the presence of someone who only talked about herself, the beauty specialist's voice droning out above her like a distant airplane in an empty sky. But if she was unfortunate enough to get someone who didn't feel like talking, the conversation necessarily led to Kim's origins, and she would of course have to say she was from a reservation in Montana (she had lied one time, and felt sick about it afterwards, even though it had spared her the otherwise inevitable, and she had sorta enjoyed making up a new life for herself). Which was followed by the exclamation-question, Oh you're part native american! Which was itself about seventy-percent of the time followed the comment that she had native american blood too. Her dad's / mom's grandma was [fill in the blank]. (But it was never anyone's grandpa who was the indian, something Kim after much thought assumed was directly related to the fact that indian men were still dangerous savages out for throat-slitting revenge, so what white woman would want to be with one of them, while white men were, as she was discovering, more than happy to pick up a squaw if there happened to be one around.) Sometimes there was the question as to how much blood she had, and until the Kim had moved off the reservation, she had never known what her exact fraction of blood was, it had never been necessary, she had only ever known that she was an enrolled tribal member. But now she had all these white people asking how much are you, so you have some, that's neat, that's cool, and she felt both reduced and contained at the same time, because no matter what her answer it was as if she had been fundamentally defined in some way that made her less than she felt she was. Yes at home she had been called a white girl by this or that bitch who was jealous or bitter about something or other, yes once a little girl had asked her why she didn't have brown skin like hers, yes she had been accused of any number of things, including acting white, for not going to parties when she was in high school, and even the summer after they graduated before she went off to California she wouldn't party, too much dangerous shit happened at rez parties, but this was different, at home she always had people who didn't party, she had her uncle Ray who had been sober since she was a little girl and who could make her laugh whenever he felt like, she had her dad who had not drank since she was a little girl, she had her mom telling her not to go off and start drinking or she'd end up just another statistic like her auntie Marilyn who had died at a house party before Kim was born, beautiful Marilyn whom she resembled almost as much as she did her own mom—yet during all her years growing up she had never felt like she was less than a whole indian, in particular a whole Blackfeet, but her conversations with non-indians at university had done something else. Instead of making her angry or defensive or vengeful they had made her feel small, a pale star among the many.

For Lawrence the transition was not so radical, he did not feel like an indian among a ocean of white people—there were a fair number of Blackfeet living in Silver Falls—he did not have to, the way Kim did, find his bearings among the very real flood tide of franchise America circling your encampment (at that time, which is clearly not this time, only a small number of businesses were not locally owned, locally operated, a phrase that itself that hadn't yet gained any currency), and neither did he feel, as Kim often did, like a diver in an old diving bell, deep in the ocean, far from the surface, at the end of his line: he was only a few hours from LaFleur, he could go home every weekend before practices started (which he did; he didn't own a car, but someone he knew was always going home), but after that, when the excitement of being in a new place had worn off, and the deeper currents of loneliness began to set in, if he found himself in the midst of a particularly bad Tuesday night all he had to do was bum a ride, or if he was desperate hop on the bus, and head out to Wal Mart, where if he did not run into a friend or relative making their last stop before hitting the freeway back to LaFleur, then at the very least he would see other indians, and just walking up and down the long aisles seeing someone from another tribe pushing a cart, holding up a bath mat, taking another set of hangers off the rack, comparing the price of one spatula to another—the sight was enough to set his heart at ease. He could go back to his dorm room, where his roommate from Stafford, who was also on the team, a guy with a farmer's tan who played the three or the four spot, was usually smoking weed and watching youtube vids, laughing his ass off at some dumb shit Lawrence didn't think was funny. They had known each other from before, had played against each other several times in the summer State Games, had tracked each other's stats the years both of them were on varsity, had played on the same starting five during the Senior Showcase, had played against each other in the state championship game, Stafford beating LaFleur by 8 in front of a crowd that must have made the seeming handful of white Montanans feel the indian uprising was at hand—the game had been tied most of the way, back and forth right up to the last minute, when a ref who had a reputation for not liking LaFleur or its players or indians in general had fouled Lawrence out of the game with the kind of loose ball foul that forced the tourney organizers to have security escort the officials off the floor, guard the doors to their locker room, and later escort them to their cars. And while he found that no one asked him how much indian blood he had, he did not irregularly hear comments from others that he must be a full-blood, what with his hair and his skin and his general looks, which, he began to realize, brought him cachet with certain white girls. Back home he had never had any more or less difficulty than any other ballplayer with enough guts to tell a girl what he thought about her, but this was different. There was a type of white girl who gravitated to him, he made no effort, she simply came to him. The first time it happened he took it as great luck, her name was Shauna, she was from Billings, she had dated this Cheyenne guy in high school so, as she said, she got the whole indian thing. They hooked up, had fun for bit, she wanted more, he couldn't see himself with a white girl (not what he said; instead he ignored her, and heard later from one of her friends that he had broken her heart) and moved on. A few of those and he got the hang of things. In the beginning there were questions—what was it like growing up in LaFleur, did he feel weird being the only indian on the team, had he ever been with a white girl before, and so on. And while he did not think they knew it, what they asked and how they asked it revealed much about them. (It is a strange truth about questions, that in asking them the interrogator becomes vulnerable.) And later, if he allowed her to get close, or sooner if she was one of those women who moved through the world like an attack dog, then came the statements. Why would you need a scholarship, you guys get everything for free anyway. Whenever you drink you turn into an indian. You're not any different than me. He found you didn't begin to know someone until you got here, to the moment when she began to tell you how the world was. He was a novelty, and he was fine with that because it meant getting laid, and these girls were a variation on a familiar theme—the spoils of athletic privilege. He had fun. He dreamed about home and his grandpa often, and waking up from dreams in which he had returned to LaFleur and everything was exactly as he had left it but no one knew his name and seemingly never had. The occasional still half-shot white girl (even if they had been seeing each other for more than a few weeks he saw her as someone belonging to that other side of the line) was not enough to transport him out of the heavy, sucking feeing that surrounded him when he woke from such dreams. The girls were sand bags tossed out before the incoming tsunami.

And then there were his coaches. Talking to him like he maybe didn't understand complicated English sentences (as if they were so complex themselves, with their monaural vision of the world: if there was something other than ball out there, they didn't care; if there were people unlike themselves they hadn't heard of them). Calling him out for his mistakes in front of the team like he was the only one fucking up. Taking him aside to explain blown plays when often enough the errors were a full-on team effort. After their first full scrimmage of the season, (the one time during every practice the guys finally remembered why they had come to this school in the first place) the head coach, Harry Muster, had called Lawrence to his office, where the rest of the coaching staff was waiting. They talked to him about keeping his grades up (he had graduated from LHS with a 3.7), they asked him how he was making the adjustment to being away from home (My heart really hurts for my grandpa, he said, a less perfunctory answer than they had wanted.) and then coach said he was going to get real with Lawrence. He only wanted a few things: stay sober, keep his grades up, and learn some discipline. We just want you to know we're concerned about how you're doing, Coach said, and we want you to do well. We know you have the potential to be a great asset to this program. Then, as if an interpreter was needed, the assistant coach offered a reiteration of Muster's request, the difference being that this time Lawrence was referred to as Chief. On their way out of the locker room the assistant put his arm around Law's wide shoulders and laughingly told him all he needed to do was give up his savage ways. Then he slapped him on the back and they each went their own way. Lawrence knew the coaches had heard from a campus cop that he was getting high the other night out behind the auxiliary gym, but they didn't seem overly concerned that his roommate had been there too, or that the fucker was about to turn green with all the weed he was smoking. He wanted to tell the coaching staff they should be glad he wasn't smoking meth. Then he laughed, because it was such a rugged thing to say, but he felt better, too, because sometimes the world away from the reservation seemed light and unreal, unmoored from anything he recognized as substantial.

There was only one other indian donning a uniform in the name of continued USF glory—she was this Assiniboine from Fort Peck, Tania, a pg with a pretty crossover and an outside shot she could get off even with a defender hanging all over her. She lived off campus with her man, a guy from her rez who didn't seem to do much besides lie around and watch game shows at their apartment, or one of a stack of dvd rentals he grabbed from the last rental place in Silver Falls, waiting for her to come home. One night at a party she was talking to Law out back of the house in the alley, sharing a cigarette—Oh, I said I wasn't going to do this during the season!—asking him how was he. All right, he thought all the time about going home, but practice and homework were his world. You know how it is, he said. I don't think I'm going to stay, she said. She listed a litany of difficulties, almost all of which Lawrence recognized as his own, including but not limited to: her teammates seemed to care about all sorts of things she didn't give a fuck about; she wasn't able to laugh with them the way she wanted to, and forget teasing them, you couldn't tease white people the way you wanted to, they either got pissed off or thought you were being mean; and she was tired, only a few games into the season, of her coaches trying to turn her into some whitewashed (my words) version of herself so she would fit better into the scheme. We aren't even good, she said, and laughed. We aren't even gonna win anything anyway. He listened. Her words, shaped on a reservation across the state from his own, filled an absence he only remembered was there when he called home and talked to one of his friends who had not left LaFleur. I don't like it, he said. She asked him what. They way they talk to us, he said. Makes me angry, you know? She did know. He was quiet for a moment. She watched him. He handed her the cigarette. Tells us who we are though, enit. What do you mean? she said. I mean, he said, it's good to know what you are.

2

A year later I sat in the back row of this class on tribal sovereignty, Kim at the front because where else do the A students sit, Law a few seats down to my right, along with the other skins who still weren't sure high school had ended. We had all transferred to U at Riverside, a few hours south of our reservation. Kim had got all homesick way down there in Califor-Ny-Ay, coming home at the start of summer wearing that mix of off-rez arrogance and confusion you will see on people who leave thinking they are better than us and return for reasons that aren't entirely clear even to themselves. Law was in Riverside because he quit the team at USF and dropped out, probably because as we all know indians can't hack it in the world of real basketball. As for me, I had finished up a double Associates at our tribal college at home, walking out head held high with one degree in Tribal Treachery and Nepotism, and another in Casino Management with an emphasis in Fucking Your People Over. I was shaking my head and smiling because this white kid a few rows up was asking about blood quantum, trying to understand its history, how it worked, the contemporary implications— unassumingly direct questions, the kind only a white kid would ask, because every indian knows you don't talk publicly about blood quantum, not unless you got some niggas who got yo back. The prof was hemming and hawing his way through, walking back and forth in front of the room, his hands behind his back, rubbing his hands together behind his back trying not to offend any of us indian students. I had to hand it to the guy—he knew his crowd. Never said anything he knew would turn us against him, always talk the good talk, always show how bad he feel for the poor historically and contemporaneously oppressed sisters and brothers. Some of the other skins in class ate that ish up, turned their brown eyes toward the great white savior at the front of the room, loved hearing another white man tell us how the world works forever and ever amen. I saw his game right away, but I let it go, because let's be honest—there's no stopping this ship from sinking. Besides. The guy put on a good puppet show. Moments of drama. Firelight flickering on the cave walls. Etc., etc.

Anyway—this white kid had asked these questions, and he had that incredulous look on his face that said he couldn't believe we weren't talking about blood quantum, given that we were all in this class to discuss American Indian sovereignty, and since this whole blood thing pretty clearly drastically affects tribal membership, and since you can't vote unless you're a tribal member, and since voting seems to have a lot to do with politics, and because politics seem to be pretty closely connected to citizenship and sovereignty...well this guy thought this was something we needed to be talking about. (Intelligent white people get the craziest ideas sometimes.) And the prof was up there stumbling through his brief history of blood quantum, talking in a different tone of voice than he usually did, none of that big-toned, bombastic stuff about treaty abrogation and ignored or violated rights, instead he was kind of going through it fast like he just wanted to get the moment over with. From the back of the room you will see a lot of things you can't see from up front, like being in the back row at the movie theater, and one of the things you can see is how people start to move around when they get uncomfortable, and you can see how the prof's body language changes, when he starts to lose confidence because he no want get throat cut by wild savage—I was watching the room get real quiet in one way, and real loud in another way. For example, this Blackfeet guy to my left who was always going off about breeds and mixed-bloods and how there could be no greater blessing than to rid turtle island of anyone who didn't have indian blood (his last name was Ramirez; there is no way to talk about blood in our language the way we talk about blood in English; and Blackfeet have never called this place turtle island; what can I say, indians are confused these days)—well this guy was one of the people who got quiet, like an animal that can feel the hunter's bullet before the trigger has been pulled. Whereas the handful of white kids in class were getting loud, raising their hands and asking questions because this blood stuff is fascinating and terrible when you look into it, and while most indians can't see beyond their own pitiful, fractionated-blood pride, most white kids figure out pretty quick there is something wrong here.

So I pull the kid aside after class. I tell him we should talk. He says he's into it. We go to a café near campus and we talk. I answer every question he has—and he has a lot. He is trying to understand how blood quantum works. What the deal is with 1/4, 1/2, full blood, all these ideas of blood. We talk about how there is no scientific basis for this idea of blood quantum, that science is so far beyond this blood quantum it's not even funny, but that it's not a new thing for indians buying into something that went out of style 80 years ago, just look at the haircuts on reservations. I tell him where these ideas come from because I know, I've done the research. So we discuss 19th Century scientific racism, which he is familiar with, but which he had no idea had affected indian people, and he is, like anyone with half a brain, taken aback to see ideas so racist and outmoded functioning in a legal setting. He is shaking his head and laughing the whole time. Well I guess we should just forget about contemporary genetic research, he says. That's true, I say. Then he asks how it is that I know so much about this when the other native american students in class don't. I like to know things, I say. Sounds to me like you've to a political career ahead of you, he says. Not for me, I say. Why not? he says. Too much work, I say. We laugh. Then I talk about the way the idea of blood was developed here as a way to help justify the theft of indigenous land, the destruction of indigenous culture, boarding schools, allotment of indian land—in other words we talk about everything that we've learned about in class, but have never really been able to discuss in a meaningful way because the prof is less worried about the truth than he is about his own pretty neck. I say I don't envy him, being a white guy up there in front of a bunch of indian students telling them about their own history. But I also say I don't know what he expected, getting into the field he did. We laugh again. The kid asks me if I want another coffee. I do, of course, because he's buying. I go the full valley girl, venti skinny mocha frappuccino but keep the whipped cream. Our new coffees fuel further discussion. I'm feeling good because indians always feel good when they meet a white person who will let them talk. The kid asks me why we use this system to identify ourselves when it comes from such a fucked up place. I tell him I have no idea, but if you are looking for a world that makes sense don't go looking for that world in indian country. But then I tell him in all seriousness it's simple, once you understand how the boarding schools worked, the way indian religious practices were outlawed, the way tribal councils were set up, the way the American concept of economy was forced on us, how the church infiltrated our communities the way the CIA infiltrates pretty much everyone, the way congress has for all intents and purposes unmitigated control of indian country, the way the only good indian isn't so much a dead indian as an indian who keeps his mouth shut...then it's pretty simple, I say, the situation becomes eminently clear. He nods. It's goddamn fucking simple, I say, and you'll never come across anything more complicated in your goddamn life. He laughs and says he's beginning to get that impression. Then he asks about indians who don't meet enrollment requirements—what happens to them? I tell him they are pretty much fucked and we laugh again. Then I tell him Law isn't enrolled. I know it's an asshole thing to do, to talk about something so personal when he is not around, but who cares, I am going the full public indian on this one, I am the authority on everything and anything indian related. He says, about Law, I just figured because of the braid...and, you know...I mean, the way he looks...and he trails off. You and every indian ever, I say. He laughs. I tell him it has taken him all of twenty minutes to figure out what indian people will apparently never figure out. I tell him that we can talk about this all day, but the truth is if he wants to know, he will have to walk the dark halls of history himself. There is more than I can ever explain to him, I say, and if he really wants to understand this he should just come crash on my couch for the next three decades. Worse things have happened, he says. We both laugh. But here is the thing to remember, I say. I lean toward him, and he leans toward me. Indian people will sell off every last bit of sovereignty for the sake of skin color alone, I say. And that's the simple truth of the matter. As long as we have people who look the way Americans think indians should look we will let the rest go to hell in a hand basket. People will say otherwise, but just try and put a blonde-haired, blue-eyed indian up in front of them. See what happens, I say. You might as well cut a person's jugular and throw him into a pool full of sharks.

I am really getting off on this conversation by now, I have wrested all control of this conversation with minimal effort. I begin to see why some indians love talking to well-meaning white people, why some indians make a career out of talking to white people. They'll let you say anything is why. They let you have the talking stick as long as you want is why. Go ahead, ask me about tribal people in a distant geographic location. I know the answer. Ask me about historical culture I have no experience with. I know the answer. Ask me about the future of indigenous people globally—I know it all. There is nothing some indians love more than being able to finally tell a white person how the world is, and I am definitely one of those indians.

But the kid, he keeps giving me that look of familiar confusion. He says he just cannot believe there is a situation like this, where someone born and raised in a place cannot vote on political processes. I say voting isn't that big of a deal, most people at home don't vote anyway, to which he says most Americans don't vote either but that doesn't make it ok to take away the right. I tell him he has a good point. Then we reach that time in the conversation where the white kid asks the question. The one question to which every conversation about indian country leads no matter where it starts or where its meanderings take us: What can be done to change this? And then, is there something he can do? There's nothing he can do, I say. Even if he had the best solution in the world, even if he had a solution that would actually fix this Pandora's box there would be nothing he could do. I tell him there is nothing he can do because he is white, and we have had enough of white people telling us what to do. To which he says, What about this class we are in. Touche, I say. But then I point out we are not really learning what to do, we are only learning history. Anyone can teach history, I say. Only an indian can show us what to do, because only an indian has seen the beast from the inside, and only an indian has been knocked around enough by the beast to feel the need to retaliate. Either an indian or some rare Jew who knows the other side, the legal side of the story and still feels enough of the persecutional sting to see how it might be for us. But as for white guys talking to us about treaties, it's all just novelty and guilt, you'll have to trust me on that one. The indians who teach, though, they know what's on the line, they know how this game plays out, they aren't talking clever about how confusing federal policy is, they are standing up there in front of us as living examples of the repercussions of all this bullshit. And as for us indians in the class, we are there to figure out what to do about our fucked up politics. We are there because we want to change things, plain and simple. Research papers are not enough. Fancy talk about contemporary ironies resulting from colonization is not enough. We want practical knowledge, and we all know what happens to desires like that in academia, for better and for worse, I say. The kid nods his head, he gets it, the fucker is smart. When it's finally time for us to leave he gives me this smile and says the other thing white people always say after this conversation: When are you going home to fix all this? I laugh and tell him I'll think about it, which is a lie, because the distance between knowledge and action in indian country is nigh unbridgeable, and I am not the one to make that sisyphean effort. But I don't let him in on that part. No—we part ways like this, and for the rest of his life that kid gets to think I am one of the difference makers, which is another way of saying at least one of us has hope.

The three of us hung out a lot in Riverside. Sometimes Kim would drive us across town so we could eat at this barbecue place. Sometimes Law would crash at my apartment after we got so high he didn't want to move, maybe ever again. Sometimes we would go to parties, those almost all-native parties, where the only white kids brave enough to hang out were either white kids from the rez or white kids who didn't cry when you teased them. Loud indian parties where everyone is having a great time waiting for some fucker to get so drunk he takes his shirt off and tries to fight someone. Sometimes I would call Kim a white girl just because I knew she would respond. I didn't care if she hated me. I've always felt that once you fucked a woman well she really couldn't say much to hurt you. You had got what you needed; her economic leverage was gone. There were other indian girls I knew who wouldn't blink if I said that shit, girls even more light-complected than Kim, girls who were more apt to spit on me or tell me to fuck off or maybe slash my tires (if they were drunk enough, if I had a car) than listen to another bullshit word from me. But the Kim at those parties was not the girl who went off to the fancy school in Cali—now she was all jittery like a spooked horse, she had seen some part of the world and herself she did not want to see. She had a story to tell and its unspooling would be her life.

Me and Law played cards a lot, most often at Smiley Jackson's place just off the edge of the U district. We would be drinking, somebody always had a cigar because that's what you do when you play cards. Sometimes if I got drunk enough I would stare at Law for a while, to let him know what was coming. When the mood finally struck I would say, Fuck I bet you wish you were enrolled, enit. Big smile. Stare at him through squint eyes. Lean into that enit so he feel it real good. But Law was not the kid who had gone off to Silver Falls to play ball—you could not get at him so easy as before, he spoke less, and sometimes there was a look he had that said he was thinking about things more than a man should. I knew other unenrolled indians, some were my own relatives, but most had little to say, they had agreed to the terms set before them, they were timid and swinging the hammer the way they were taught. But Law was different, because his grandpa was different. A few years before the old guy had got people together, tried to get rid of our blood quantum laws—and he had almost pulled it off. Only some last minute, under the table dealings with the tribal council (my own mother being under that table) causing the rescinding of a resolution put the dream to rest. When you are close to something like that, when you are next to a person with the courage to do what his grandpa had done you are changed, the way someone who has stood next to a fire is changed. When you have seen someone close-up take the public battering ram and not flinch I believe you see a kind of life the rest of us do not see, a life apart from the pettiness and the fear. But his time in Silver Falls had shown him something about where he fell in the grand American order, and he was just young enough to confuse what his grandpa had shown him with that more common indian rage. And I was just old enough to see how I might get what I wanted out of such a situation.

But don't let me fool you—laziness is the quality most often found holding hands with intelligence. I knew my mom and the others (two of whom were Kim's parents) opposed to Law's grandpa were small in stature and limited in vision. I watched them and saw they were like old blind dogs barking at sounds in the night. I went to school and took native studies courses and studied history found them guilty of acting as mouthpieces for long dead white congressman with political and cultural extinction agendas on their minds. I sat in meetings and bore witness to the sins they committed against their own people. I felt the surge of power in my blood when they discussed how they would destroy Law's grandpa's agenda. I felt the thrill when they celebrated their victory. Our victory. I remember well how Kim's mother had looked, screaming at anti-enrollment-reform rallies in front of the tribal offices, talking her megaphone talk about how we needed to keep color in the tribe, how we couldn't allow people with hardly a drop of indian blood to vote, to take our jobs from us, to take our fifteen-dollar per capita checks from us. I remember well her anti-blonde, anti-blue-eyed, anti-white rhetoric, that light-complected woman with her brown hair and her gray eyes. I remember thinking I wouldn't mind a few more blondes in the tribe, so long as they weren't my cousins.

3

First time we see her that summer after learning how politically fucked we are is up at the outdoor pool behind the big lodge that had been built in the 1920s for the sole purpose of bringing white people to our reservation so they could then go on into the national park that had belonged to us only two decades or so before, but had been for all intents and purposes removed from our jurisdiction as the educated like to say. She wears a red bikini with white polka dots all over, and has those oversized sunglasses that for some reason speak to me of lollipops and blowjobs. Her friend is there with her, I can't remember her first name, she was an Eagle Child, she is dead now a long time. Their bodies glisten in the sun. Other than the four of us everyone in and out of the pool is white. Kim and the Eagle Child girl got in (Lodge Guests Only) because the lifeguard, one of the many kids from out of state come to our reservation to drink and get laid and hike into our mountains, has a thing for Kim. Me and Law get in because we walk in like the last 300 years did not happen. Kim all light brown and beautiful with her heart-shaped face and perfect teeth and the other dark and beautiful with her wide and vaguely Asiatic face, both of them lie on their towels on the white beach chairs, the hot concrete reflecting the sun back to itself. Me and Law had been driving around looking for ass, we had come down the highway from LaFleur to the big lodge because we knew all the girls in LaFleur, they arrived in our field of vision as insignificant or we were related to them. Me and Law, cousins starting back six or eight generations with Ninnastako and his previous names and his 5 wives and his many children, he being known to us all through that single photo of him sitting in a metal folding chair grim-faced in his warbonnet and buckskins, not looking at the camera at all, looking toward his own death, and probably backward to that moment when the first white man arrived traveling under an air-warping cloud of dark premonition. I say they are coming to a party with us later. Kim sits up and raises her sunglasses and squints at me. The Eagle Child girl leaning back on her elbows. Her belly button ring flashing in the sun. Are we? Kim says. We'll pick you up at your parents' place tonight, I say, unless California's still got you thinking you're too good. They laugh. You can feel Law drilling holes into Kim with his dark eyes. We drive around for a while, get some beer and some forties. We drink and I tell Law he had got all serious since he come back from Silver Falls and what was the deal. He doesn't say anything, he just half-smiles and takes a drink. I say I don't fucking care anyway, caring was for pussies and while we are many things we are not pussies. Cousin, I say, you can shoot up a theater full of white people for all I care so long as I'm not there when you do it. He laughs.

That night at the bonfire by the lake he is still drilling holes into Kim with his eyes. The lifeguard is there too trying to act smooth, but what white guys like that never figure out is whatever smooth they got hits our women like a cheese grater. Later on I find him utterly ripped out of it, stumbling around with no woman at all. I pop him once, twice, just to make it worse for him, while he is pissing, just to see what he will do, out away from the firelight so I don't get jumped by a bunch of his boys. He doesn't do much but whimper. That night is the first time Kim and Law hook up. They sit close on a piece of driftwood, she leans into him and throws her head back and laughs the way a woman does when she wants a guy to know she is into him. I had seen it during the last year in Riverside, that California had shown her something the other girls on the reservation had never seen. Without even trying she shined, soft and easy and light, like bubbles floating in a white person's front yard in one of those filmsc where nothing really happens, where people talk and hurt each others feelings and slam doors. So I talk with other girls, I don't look at Kim and Law at all, I am the indian guy talking to the white girls in the summer dark, flashing my exotic smile and drinking hard and making them laugh. I set my sights on a little hippie girl from Mississippi come up to the northern plains to work and see the savage indians, no makeup, more clean cut than she wishes, got that private school smile, got that trust fund smile, got that smile say she like the indian boy. Despite the usual minor protestations we fuck in the back end of her Land Rover (she's got the back seat removed). I drive us back to town and stay with her in her dorm room at the big lodge. I hitchhike back to LaFleur the next morning, picked up by my cousin Mike, both of us telling the kind of rugged jokes you only tell when you're driving with your cousin in the a.m. and both of you are still about half-shot.

Kim and Law keep going. On the regular as the niggas used to say on TV. They drive around in her car cause Law ain't got nothing but his grandpa's old red Ford and his grandpa usually needs to drive to work early so he can drive bus for middle school kids attending summer Blackfeet cultural programs. In the beginning it's just the hook up, just meeting and driving most often up to the lake and fucking. There is this pull-off a mile or so past where the bonfire was. They go there. Only locals know about this pull-off. Kim and Law would park across the highway from the start of the trail and go down and fuck, sometimes not even making it all the way down to the edge of the lake, just going off the side of the trail and throwing a blanket down and doing it. This is that phase where little is said, and what is said is like birdsong in the morning when the sun is coming up, or like sunlight when it first hits the rooftops of a Spanish coastal city where I am sure love happens often and the echoes of the Inquisition is all but gone. Sometimes they go to the lake in the mornings, if neither is working. (She works as barista for white people who travel from all parts of the globe to see the mountains which are somehow not ours but will always be ours. She wonders each day if the men and sometimes women who ogle her are doing so because she is beautiful to them, or because she is the little indian princess in their midst, waiting to be saved from the darkness of reservation life. Law works at one of the entrance stations to the national park whose boundaries separate the mountains from our reservation, demarcating them as federal territory. Demarcating them as not ours. He wears a wide-brimmed, Smokey the Bear hat and takes money from people who have come to see the mountains. None of these people can see Law's tattoos, the ones he picked up during the last year at Riverside. So we can say at least one thing came from all that sovereignty talk: his left shoulder is adorned by our ten-thousand-plus-years name, the name we had before some white guy decided to call us Blackfeet, and we agreed: Piikunii. (Fuck this Blackfeet shit, he had told me.) The right shoulder is adorned by his grandpa's indian name, which will be given to him many years after the time of this story: Nobody's

Gun.) So if they are not working they go down to the edge of the lake and they strip and swim. Kim would take off her shirt and her shorts and her bra and goes in like that, hesitant even though she wants to go faster because she knows being scared of the water is the sort of things girls are supposed to do. But she also knows that Law will splash her if she goes in slow, and she wants that but doesn't want it. Sometimes he pulls her down into the water, almost tackling her as if she were a guy, because he was what, twenty. If they swim out they go out far enough that they reach the line where the water becomes dark, and they stop there. If either goes beyond that line, usually it is Law, then he doesn't go far, there is that old fear of the deep water in them that comes from the old people who did not venture into deep water and did not spend time on lakes and did not build canoes. Other times they do not go into the water, they stay on the thin bar of sand between the trees and brush and the thirty feet or so of rocks that lead to the water's edge. In the mornings the water is even colder than normal, and their bodies are shocked by the cold, and their bodies are covered in goose bumps, and their skin feels tight, and her nipples stand out from her breasts, and the sight of her is enough to make the world disappear. Other times they go down to the lake in the evening, maybe even after dark, and despite the knowledge that bears are known to travel that length of beach they do not carry that pepper spray every white person seems to carry even if they are only driving into the mountains. Should we be thinking about bears, she says. My grandpa said bears don't go after us, he says. Nonetheless there are times when they go down the trail that he wonders about the truth of this, and fear spreads out from some place deep inside of himself, out through his limbs to the surface of his skin like sheet lightning touching the surface of the earth. If they go down to the lake at night then the water reflects the moon and often this is the only time of day when the water is still. (Because the memory of beauty outlasts even the memory of pain she will remember long after all this is over his wide, graceful shoulders, his smooth chest lit by the cool, pale light, his angular face as yet uncut by time.) If the wind blows in the summer, even if only a breeze, then it does so during the day—the night brings stillness. You can hear animals on the opposite shore, where there are no nearby roads, a single broken branch sounds out through the trees at the base of the mountains, and across the surface of the lake. You can hear it enter the water, its legs breaking the surface of the water. You will never know what it is.

Sometimes when they fuck at night he covers her mouth because he does not want her to make any sound anything else can hear. Once when he covered her mouth she began to feel a drawing need in her chest, a panic came over her like a breeze so slight the heart-shaped aspen leaves hanging above their bodies would not have stirred. She throws his hand away. That night she dreams she is in the lake by herself, she had swum out to the line where the water becomes dark, and it is night. There is a moon and then there is not a moon and then there is a moon again. On the other shore she hears a woman singing a calling song. She knows it is some part of herself calling back to her but they will not be meeting again. Then she is walking off the beach into the woods but the trail up is hard to follow and she knows she did not park her truck above because there was no road anyway and she did not arrive by vehicle, she has always been here. Pretty soon she is lost and panic overtakes her but instead of turning back to the lake she pushes deeper into the forest, in part because she knows the lake is gone now and she is in the forest for good, in part because she knows that if she were to go back she would find someone waiting on the beach for her. She moves further in. She passes through places of darkness, she passes through places where the moonlight falls through the trees and dapples the forest floor.

Law quits his job at the entrance station to work at the pawn shop in downtown LaFleur. He says he got tired of being the indian guide, there to greet the white man as he enters the heart of our spiritual territory. Just think, he says, when those people are driving into our mountains they are driving into our heart. I consider it, and discard what he's said because the thought makes me feel sad and helpless. He works mornings at the pawn shop, and sometimes I go in to hang out. The white guy who owns the shop and lives off the reservation doesn't care, most mornings he is not even there, his wife is there, she is nervous and makes all the employees nervous. She tried to kick me out once because she thought I was just some loitering indian waiting to steal something, I'm sure, but I sweet talked my way through the moment, and after that when I show up to bullshit Law she says hi and a few times she asks if I want a job. When I'm there I lean on the counter and me and Law talk about the usual—ass, is there a party, did you hear what happened. He sits in the back where the saddles and ropes and various other cowboy accouterment are. Law sitting in the back with his braid and his serious face looking at the gun case on the adjoining wall, looking at John Wayne posters because the owner of course has a thing for The Duke. One day on his break he takes me down to the case and starts telling me which ones he wants, he is thinking about putting some money down and setting up a payment plan, something he can do as an employee. I laugh and say he is going to turn into one of those militant skins wearing transitions, and who has a lifetime supply of red bandannas. He doesn't laugh. He says did I know that because he is not enrolled the rangers at the park entrance station have tried to deny him access to the mountains. Think about that, bro, he says. This is what it's come to, he says. We go from owning the mountains some ten thousand years to a guy like me not even being able to get in under treaty rights. Well, I say, we didn't really own them the way we use that word now. You know what I mean, he says, and besides, that kind of ownership is the valid way to talk about this stuff anymore. I nod in agreement. Anyway, he says, those motherfuckers talk to me like I'm trying to rip them off when all I want is to drive into the mountains. Our mountains. You're right, I say, it's fucked—but what can you do? We gotta do something, he says. We gotta drink, I say. We got a bonfire party to go to, I say, white girls everywhere. I got a girl, he says, and I'm tired of partying. He leans on the gun case, both palms down on the glass. I think about his palm prints on the glass. This one, he says. He nods at a pistol whose name and type I forget the moment he tells me, because I have never been one of those guys who gets a hard-on over guns, and because I am hungover. He presses a finger against the glass. I want that one, he says.

One night when I am at the grocery store I run into her mom. She is one of those women who is pretty but hard, and when you talk to her you feel you are talking to a shell, and what is beneath is not something you can trust. She gets my number and says she wants to talk to me that night. She calls a few hours later to ask who Kim is with. I don't think she is seeing anyone, I say. She tells me not to lie and I say I am not lying. She says she trusted me to tell her the truth since she knew Kim and I were friends. I say I tell only the truth so help me god and I laugh. A few days later we are at an after-party, this lousy jam band had played on stage out behind this bar up on the northwest part of the reservation in a little town called Riel (everyone says Reel), but it is not even really a town, just a few tribal housing houses and the lousy bar and some other houses up in the woods close to the mountains. I would never go up there except that I knew there would be white girls everywhere, and there is always some white girl who love the indian boy. I see them near the stage each drinking from a shared red plastic cup. She is laughing. He has that sly mean look on his face because he had probably just said something rugged. Law was that kind of guy, not loud but really smart with a serious case of Blackfeet humor. I find a white girl with a great ass. She goes by the name of Juniper. I fail in my attempt to procure her. She had flirted with me and had put her hands on me and I had gotten my hands on her but then she was gone. I look around for a few minutes, getting myself a drink in the meantime. I find her leaving the concert grounds with this group of white kids who must have been her crew, and when I put my hand on her arm she shrugs me off, and when I say her name she laughs like she has never met me. Her friends look at the indian boy like he rape nice white girl all time. I see myself crushing their skulls with rocks. Stand over them with bloodied rocks in hand and bellow like the conquering savage. #4real2. I text her mom see yr daughter making out w this guy rite now lol. She replied but I ignore her until the next afternoon, reading over her seven 2:30 a.m. texts a few times for a good laugh. We go back and forth a bit, and I finish by saying I did not recognize the guy but figured I should tell her since she was asking. Then I ignore her for a few days because I feel like it, not even reading her texts and feeling good about it.

Me and Law are out cruising around LaFleur and drinking and I am talking about women and he is quiet, only halfway into the ass talk. So is she good or what, I say. He just smiles and shakes his head. Well come on, I say, you can't leave a cousin hanging. It ain't like that, he says. I laugh. You think this is going any further than what you got now? I say. I take a long drink and drive us up toward the tribal offices just because. Fuck man, you gotta get as much from her as you can while you can, cousin. A fancy girl like that ain't sticking around for a rez dog like you, I say. He smiles and shakes his head, the way he would when he was hurt and didn't know what to do. I don't know if there is truth to what I am saying, but sometimes you feel the need to hurt something, so you do. After that night Law keeps his distance for a while, ignores calls, answers one out of three texts, always busy, etc. Fine. Cause I got other cousins to hang out with. Kim and Law get closer, spend more time together, maybe because what I said awoke the ancient fear of losing the woman, or maybe, like most of the time, because of things I will never understand.

They still go to the lake all the time. Still fuck all time. By now the midsummer sun has dried out the earth and the people are seeking nearby water, cars stacked up at bridges pull-outs or lined up along the highway where no pull-outs, brown kids in cheap swim suits and basketball shorts maybe someone with a hatchback got the back end open hip hop or country or both each taking a turn blasting out of pawn shop speakers and bass cannon. The sun hot already by mid-morning, the plains gone brown til next year, the wind hot on your face and arms afternoons while you shoot free-throws out behind the old highschool, ten feet from the only rim somewhat unbent, absentee net, one out of one, two out of two, three out of three, three out of four, three out of five, four out of six. Maybe a few guys show up looking for a game of twenty-one. You win, you don't win, it doesn't matter, the heat and the dull sound of the ball on the metal backboard matters, the ricocheting sound of the dribbled ball off the nearby brick school exterior matters, so hot no talking is done, there is only the game, bandannas, bad fadeaways, shoes shredded from a summer of this. You wait for your cousin, your main man, the guy you taught how to crossover, the guy who passed you up in glorious fashion, although you would never tell him this—you hope he will show up to play some real ball, because he knows how it is, he played in the college air but the asphalt is where he made himself. He knows this is still the only real kind of ball ever played or ever will be played. More free-throws. You walk home to your gram's house which now belongs to you because she deeded it to you before she died, across the street from Old Low Rent, where you remember as a boy seeing an old woman grieve, her husband had died, she had put her kitchen chair out on the grass and she was grieving. A sound you had never heard before and have not heard since came from her mouth, a repetitive wailing sound deeper than any grief you yet know of that strikes a place just behind your ribs and opens up like a golden star. You are standing on the sidewalk. You ask yourself how such power can come from such a small, bent body. You listen until your gram takes you by the arm and pulls you inside. When you ask her what the woman is doing, she says she is grieving, that is how a woman used to do it when her man died. Except that she would got out of the camp, maybe up on a ridge nearby, and she would do that, and everyone in the camp could hear. Four days like that she would fast and then she comes back, and she might have cut herself across her arms like this. What if it was winter? Even in winter. You lay awake that night and sometimes you could still hear the old woman, you are thinking about her sitting there alone in that metal folding chair. Then a few weeks later she is dead too, and you have never heard or seen such a thing again. That was the summer you stayed with your gram because your mom and dad had split and the fighting was so bad your gram took you, just said she was taking you with her, and walked out of your parents' place.

They still go to the lake but not as often. The sun rises later, sets earlier. Her mother has been talking to her about him. Kim does not know how the woman found out who it was but she did. Of course secrets in indian country are only secrets because they are new. They talk more and fuck less. Sometimes they lie in the back of her truck and hold each other, and the feel of each other's bodies is not the short route to eros it was even two months ago. Kim tries not to tell him what her mom is saying but he makes her, he can tell she is not saying something, and when she does he listens stone-faced and calm in a way she does not like. She falls into him more often, wanting to push herself against him in some attempt to fuse with him and forget her day of serving iced lattes. She pushes her face into his chest or his neck. She realizes that he says we in a way she has never been able to say we. That in fact until she had spent a year in Cali where there were few indians around in a per capita kind of way she had never been urged by context alone to use we. Maybe it was all the prying questions, albeit well-meaning most of the time but still, the questions that wanted to open her up like an archaeology site and dig around in her guts. She learned something about being an indian in America during that year, she was alone amidst a tide of white people, she found herself hanging out with other indians just because they were indian, not even because she liked them but because it was as close as she could get to home. Returning to Montana, even to Riverside, where she could go anywhere and at least see natives, this had helped her relax. He says we with such ease she finds herself feeling left out. She considers her past, her mother's voice, realizes that her dad has always said we but her mother never has. How often her mother would use third person when talking about other indians. How her mother taught her to be an indian who only says I.

When they go to restaurants the other patrons look at him differently than they look at her. She begins to see that beauty has a set of rewards for her that have nothing to do with men wanting to fuck her or be nice to her, and that if he were only a bit prettier he would be afforded these rewards too. They sit and eat and she notices again that his features are very indian, as they say. His long braid running down the middle of his back does not help matters. His wide nose, his lips that are not thin, his massive smile that eats his face. Plus there is his walk, his strides are easy, his back is not entirely straight, he has the easy half-swagger of the athlete. And finally there is the darkness of his skin, without which all the other things, even the braid—their impact would be lessened, the way her own relative lightness acts as a kind of parachute for her wherever she goes. The contemplation that had only begun in Cali now begins to take a definite shape. She asks herself what kind of sympathy there is that might come from fucking a man, how the physical act could lead to suddenly finding that she was thinking about him when she did not expect or want to, how he had carved out a space in her heart simply by fucking her. There was danger in this thing that women and men did. That first night at the bonfire—this had not been what she had wanted, she had wanted to have fun, she had wanted to get drunk, she had wanted to lose herself in something or someone.

They keep talking about how he is not enrolled. The talk begins to take over whatever it is they have. She does not tell him the things she heard her mother say a few years earlier when his grandpa had been pushing to change enrollment requirements. She does not tell him does not tell him then she tells him. She recalls her mother's fury that these half-breeds, these mixed-bloods, these fucking blonde-haired, blue-eyed wannabes who wanted to be indian. She tells him about the cruelty in her mother's comments regarding unenrolled people. (People like me, you mean, he says.) The irrational rages the woman would fly into during that time. The way she would sneer at the pleading, pathetic tone of some of the ones who wanted to be enrolled. One time she threw a plate at the refrigerator. Kim still saw her mother standing in the bed of a truck—the same truck she had been driving all summer, the same truck she and Law had fucked in—parked in front of the tribal offices with a bullhorn to her mouth, screaming that the breeds must be floated off the reservation, that the tribal council must pass a resolution or face the consequences in that summer's coming elections. What her time with Law has done is draw out the shame she felt then, watching her light-complected mother, with her brown hair and her gray eyes, shout to a crowd of Blackfeet that people who look like her must be forcefully removed. Kim knows now such a thing would not happen— what would the tribal police force, all fifteen of them, have done against the thousands of people who would have to leave—but it was the rhetoric of the situation, it was the tone of voice, it was in the violence of her facial expressions. And it was in the way the crowd had responded to her, the way some people had cheered, there had been signs whose words and tone she had recognized when viewing slides of hate rallies from the sixties in 20th Century American History. What her unexpected feelings for Law had done was cast her mom in new and dubious light that had somehow been there the whole time. Fuck fuck fuck.

Her mother's comments of course elicit fights, the mother and daughter going after each other with that special viciousness reserved for women, her dad usually coming in to break up the warfare. Her mom always makes sure to get the last word in, even if that means talking to Kim while she is flossing or brushing her teeth so she can't really talk back. Mom in that disgusted state that invites bad syntax and mispronunciation. One time Kim leaves the house and drives across town to Law's but he is gone, so she heads up to the big lodge to see if any of her coworkers are around for a drink, and she is relieved not only to find that several of them are, but that they are not in any way indian. At some point during the night of drinking whiskey with the girls in a dorm room she blurts out that she is very fucking glad they are white, at which the other girls kind of smile. But Kim laughs so hard their smiles become uncomfortable grimaces.

Meanwhile Law is with me, getting high as fuck—we had taken a drive and we were talking real for the first time since early summer, sitting in my car, passing the blunt I had rolled back and forth, talking about the council's continued successful impression of a circus of lobotomized monkeys despite the rotating membership. Don't matter anyway, he says, I'm never gonna vote, I got no say in that ish. I tell him being enrolled is overrated, not because I actually believe this but because the effort required to say what I really think is impossible given my condition, not to mention my general disposition. Also I had been lonely, and I did not want to piss him off. So I listen. He is telling me I do not know anything about it, he says I am just like everyone else who is enrolled, we are all suffering from that special colonized form of political laziness. All you guys say you know we should deal with this blood issue, but not now. I am quiet. Well, he says, when will that be, motherfucker? I am quiet. He explains how fucked the land inheritance system is on our reservation because of blood quantum and land being passed on to people who didn't have the blood, he explains trust and fee land even though we both know I know this already. He is saying the people who are against changing enrollment requirements have no vision, and he does not mention my mom or Kim's mom but we both know they are counted among those he is talking about. I tell him I agree, and add that not only do they have no vision, but they are ugly as fuck. He asks me what I think about white professors teaching indians about themselves. I say I have no time for such nonsense but what are you going to do, white people run the world. Then we talk about the nature of whiteness in relation to indian people, and what do people really mean when they said white or indian, because we had each noticed that the issue was far more complicated than just skin color because there were plenty of light-complected Blackfeet who were against changing the enrollment requirements and there were any number of dark-complected Blackfeet who were in favor of reform—and so what was it all about? To that you had to add that Blackfeet, and plenty of other indians we had come across, would bring out the vehement anti-white commentary only when they were pissed off, or only when it was directed at someone they didn't like. And then a day later they are hosting their best friend, a white guy, for a week-long stay at their house. Law is more engaged than I am. He is talking about his life; I am talking about something that is happening to someone else. I might as well be a white professor telling indians about themselves. I might as well be part of the latest generation of indian agents. I stop talking for a while. I feel the thing in me begin to turn. I listen and listen and listen and then when I cannot hold back any longer I tell him what I think of he and Kim's chances. You're gonna have to let her go, niksokowa, I say. Now it is his turn to be quiet. All that arguing and what not with her mom, I say, that's just her being young. She's gonna end up thinking just like that old bitch dog anyway. People don't change, I say. I talk to him like I was Francis the Gray but in reality I was all of twenty-four then, and just old enough to see the arc of my own failure. Cousin, he says to me, I do believe you can fuck off now.

The next I hear anything about either Kim or Law is when the dad chokes out Law on main street in front of all the trucks and cars waiting at the red light. He has been up to then quiet about all of this, but has also in his own way let Law know what is up. The two had run into each other earlier in the summer when mom had first got wind of what was going on. Their meeting is in the drive thru at the Burger Shack. He had seen Law sitting passenger in Charlie Big Sun's Ford and has come up on them and stands there for a second real quiet. Law just looking at him. The window is down so her dad leans in, resting his forearm on the door, and says he doesn't want to see Law's breed ass anywhere near his girl or hear about it ever again. Her dad was not young but neither was he someone to fuck with, as he was one of those old rancher types who was still hard, and in addition to overseeing tribal housing projects he still worked with cows all the time. Always wearing a black Stetson around which a silver and turquoise band was strung. Law not saying anything just looking at her old man. He notices that she has his eyes—not always, but there were moments when she became hard, and he would tease her about this. He would say, You get that look in your eyes, you look plum fuckin mean. Her dad walks away from the truck and gets back into his own and sits there like nothing happened. He waits in line. He orders a plain hamburger with small fries. Meanwhile Charlie says, Holay bro, the fuck was that? Me and Kim been hooking up is all, Law says. Charlie asks for a high five but does not get one. So months later when her old man has him pinned up against the main-street-side wall of the only pawn shop in LaFleur under the August sun he is not surprised, his concern is only for his wind pipe, which is slowly but surely being pushed back into his spine. The old guy is strong as fuck, and Law while not small is not a fighter by comparison. There is a moment of lucidity amidst his gasping for breath when he realizes that if he lives he is going to hear about this for the rest of his life, and in a culture where people feed off the shame of others this is no small thing. The old guy lets him down of course, he has been talking to him the whole time but Law doesn't remember any of it. He has one hand at his throat and the other on his thigh, doubled over while her dad stands there quiet, his shadow eclipsing the sun so that Law feels like he is in a shadow while the rest of the world is draped in heat and light. When he finally stands up straight he tries to talk but his throat hurts so bad he stops. Her dad—Law suddenly remembers the bastard's name is Clyde —says Law is lucky he forgot his gun at home. Law thinks this memory lapse is unlikely, given how Kim has said before that her dad never goes anywhere without his guns. You don't stay the fuck away from my girl you won't ever walk regular again, he says. Then he is gone.

Law sends a text to Kim yr dad just fkn choked me!!! and waits. She says she is off work in 30 minutes, and that she has something to tell him anyway. She picks him up at his grandpa's place and they drive out toward the mountains. Neither one of them is thinking about the fact that only one hundred years earlier the mountains themselves were part of the reservation, and up to that point had been used primarily for fasting sites, but that there has been hardly a fast in the mountains since then, with park officials actively keeping Blackfeet out despite various rights being retained by treaty. This is the kind of situation where a guy in Law's position might have gone out to fast to gather his power and get clear in the head before he took action—instead he is riding shotgun in a red Dodge Ram with blacked out windows and top-forty country playing low on the stereo. Law is so furious, she has never seen him this way. She has the urge to calm him but isn't sure how while she's driving. So she listens. Her dad's behavior leaves her incredulous, both that he would do such a thing, and at herself, that despite all the conversations with Law she had not understood what this blood thing was all about until now. She has already texted her mom saying if u had anything to do with this mom we r NEVER talking again. She hasn't heard anything back. She is planning out what she is going to say to her dad when she gets home. While he can be cruel and hard and distant he has never quite been able to be so with her, his only girl. (At least the only one he ever claimed—everyone knows Kelly Hale is his girl, ten years Kim's senior, a woman with a mean face that shows the scorecard of more than a few fights. And then there is Julia Wilson, but a few month's Kim's junior, she might be his too, although her mom never knew who the dad was, but the sheer weight of the physical resemblance is enough to convince most. Neither of them are enrolled, because they are legally unclaimed their father's blood was not counted in their final total of indian blood.) When they get finally get to this pull-out on the west edge of the reservation they have been going to, a pull-out that looks down into what might be the most beautiful place within at least a thousand square miles if not more, a valley where in the days before the coming of the white man it was not uncommon for newly coupled lovers to set up their lodge at the edge of the lake, they got to know each other here, some of them may have even been Kim's or Law's distant relatives, sleeping together and listening to the sounds of the night as they echoed off the mountainsides and crossed the lake's smooth surface, this valley now designated as public land, this valley where Law has had to argue that no, he does not have to pay to get into the mountains, that despite his lack of blood he does not have to fucking pay to get into the mountains. He and Kim have been to this pull-out that looks down into this valley, that looks back into the mountains where men went to fast to wait for visions, for songs, for power—they have been here recently because the last time they were down by the lake some workers from the big lodge showed up, essentially ruining that section of the beach for them. (What they did not know was that I had shown these kids that section of beach the day before, just because.) She stops the truck and tries to calm Law by sliding over to him and putting her hands on him. They talk for a while about nothing. He gets sullen, quiet, looks out at the mountains but doesn't really see the mountains. She decides not to tell him. They drive back into town and she drops him off at his grandpa's and says she will be back later. He says nothing. When she gets to my house I'm waiting on the concrete steps, which are starting to crumble but tribal housing won't be coming to fix them anytime soon. I tell her we should go for a drive because she looks distraught. I tell her she should let me drive because she needs to relax. By the time we get out to the parking lot behind the old pencil factory a few miles out of town it is dark. I smoke her up, and once she's good and blazed she says she shouldn't be doing this, not anymore. She tells me what her dad did. I act surprised, like I had no idea such a thing might happen. Then she talks for a while about nothing and stops. Whenever someone wants to say something but won't say it, I just let them stew in their own discomfort until they spill or collapse in on themselves—the key is not to let on that you have any interest. Never let anyone know you care. I tell her to come sit by me and she does. She puts her arms around me and leans into me hard. I can tell that she is feeling pretty shattered. I ask her if this means we are going to fuck, and I laugh, but I do it in such a way that she knows, if she wants to know, that I am serious. Francis, she says, but she is not making any moves to go anywhere. I can't have a baby with Law, she says. My mom, she says. I laugh and shake my head. Because I know that just this morning Law paid off that pistol, and if I know Law he is sitting at his grandpa's place right now, on the edge of his bed, and maybe he has the gun in his hands, and maybe that lamp on his dresser is on, and maybe the lighting is dramatic, and maybe he is close to doing the sort of thing we all think about doing but never do. I laugh again. She pulls away from me. I can feel her looking at me in the dark. What's funny, she says. Nothing, I say. I want to go home now, she says.

We are all fucked is all, I say, and I laugh again, as if the world could not have been any other way.

Hands (a novel excerpt)
By Kristiana Kahakauwila

In 1999, Native Hawaiian taro farmers sued Alexander and Baldwin (AandB), the last remaining sugar plantation on Maui, over water usage. The ten-year litigation that followed became a landmark case for Water and Indigenous Rights in Hawai`i.

Henry is a retired sugar cane plantation worker who has farmed taro on the windward side of Maui his entire life. Recently diagnosed with Parkinson's Disease, Henry feels as if he is no longer useful, nor even truly alive. His daughter, Mele, who works for AandB as an engineer, wants her father to stop farming; his son, Pueo, refuses to answer Henry's beckons; only his son's best friend, Billy, wants to see Henry, returning to Maui ostensibly to reconnect, though Henry senses Billy has ulterior motives for being there. Although Henry has never been particularly political, he is about to join the fight for water rights, and this fight will change his life—and his family's—forever.

Pray. Do your exercises. Take your medicine. Eat clean. Drink water. Stretch your hands. The list goes on. Henry, his head in the refrigerator, straightens his back, pushes his chest forward and rolls his shoulders. Stand straight, he tells himself.

And cut the sodium, he adds. No Portuguese sausage, no potato chips, no salted cashews. And no beer. Strict orders on the beer. He reaches instead for a bottle of water but it slips from his hand, rolls across the kitchen floor. These hands that used to do so much—dig, plant, harvest, carry, caress—can now barely hold a bottle of water.

He closes the fridge door and the kitchen is strangely dark without the appliance light. In their bedroom Ellen murmurs to herself. She sleeps deeply, doesn't notice when Henry awakes, doesn't hear his midnight perambulations. Sometimes he walks out to the lo`i and works by moonlight. Other nights, like this one, he tries to fix himself a snack, thinks of eating it on the patio with the portable television on low, but then is stymied by the list of foods he's not supposed to consume.

He leans on the sink counter, in front of the window that overlooks the patio and yard. Above the banana grove the moon has risen and cuts a pathway to the edge of the ocean cliff that marks the end of their property. The bottle has come to rest beside his bare foot and he looks down at it, spitefully.

Just give up and die, Henry thinks. Then he is angry for pitying himself. No, he has to fight this. He has to beat the PD, or least learn to live with it. Be better than it.

He sighs. He has to sleep a single night all the way through. That would be a feat.

A light is on in the shed and for a moment Henry thinks it's a burglar. Then he remembers the hānai boy has returned home. Henry should join Billy in the shed, talk to him, tell him how it's been these past years, but he feels a distance from Billy. Instead, Henry finds his slippers and follows the empty paved road that runs the center of Ke`anae, this small windward village he calls home. He takes a shortcut between two neighbors' homes and makes his way to a cow gate. No one ever locks it. None of the neighbors own cows anymore.

There is no paved road here, just ruts in the grass from the golf cart he drives during the day. The path runs a half mile, ending at the lo`i, the paddies where he and his neighbors grow their taro. The paddies are filled with moving water, fed by a waterfall at the back of the valley. At the foot of the falls is a pool, cold and fresh, where Mele and Pueo once swam as children, for the pool was large and deep, and they could jump into it from the rocks that bordered its edge. An `auwai, or stream, runs from the pool to the lo`i, and then between each lo`i, connecting them.

The lo`i are built on the gradual decline of the valley's mouth. The highest lo`i receives the coldest mountain water, but all the taro need moving water to prevent their leaves from yellowing, their roots from failing to grow. The last paddy is built close to the village, near the cow gate, and here the mountain water is warmer than at the back of the valley, as it has been heated by its time in the sun, the work of moving among the plants. Here, too, the fresh water meets the ocean, creates a brackish river where fish fry and fresh water shrimp swim upstream to make their homes in the lo`i.

Henry kneels beside his largest taro paddy. These days there is no baby awa dart among the taro's roots. No`ōpae can be caught and boiled and eaten. He has planted only three lo`i this season and rerouted the `auwai so that the water flows only through these paddies and not the the others, which have been abandoned and left to weeds. Better to save the ones that can be saved than fail them all.

He dips his hand into the water to feel its temperature. Unlike the ocean, this water has no stickiness to it. When he withdraws his fingers, his skin feels clean and soft. He lies down on his back and rotates his ankles, one of the exercises he is supposed to do for physical therapy and one that Ellen is always harping on him to perform in bed before they fall asleep. These exercises take precedent over the activities of their youth, one kind of physical life for another.

The earth has retained the warmth of the afternoon. In the morning, when he awakes, he will feel the dampness in his joints—will be sorry he stayed there—but for now the earth is shimmering with heat. He notices how the ground is harder, drier, than it used to be years ago. The grass is hardly a bed of comfort, instead scratching at the back of his neck and knees. But he remains, staring up at the moon. In the Hawaiian calendar, these days of a young moon are good for planting. If he had the water, he'd make Billy plant another paddy. Henry knows where his strengths still lie, and being a father—having a father's power—is one of them.

He remembers when Billy first came to them. It was in the days just before his best friend's daughter's wedding—Dennis's eldest girl, Lily. Ellen was fond of Lily, had treated her like a little sister much of their lives, and Henry liked Maka, the boy Lily was marrying. Maka was hard-working, serious, and not a playboy type like some of Lily's previous boyfriends.

In preparation for the wedding celebration, Henry had dug an imu in their backyard, not far from the sea cliff where their property fell into the ocean. The pit was Mele's height but twice as wide. As he dug, Henry noticed a haole boy, blond hair cut like an upside down rice bowl, watching him. When it was time to bring the stones up from the ocean, Henry said to Pueo, "Go get dat boy, da haole one."

"He not haole dad," Pueo said.

"Eh?" Later Henry would meet the boy's mother, learn she was one of Tutu Goodwin's granddaughters, the lucky one to inherit her grandmother's property. But at that time all Henry knew was that the boy's parents were from California and that the boy looked like the kind to get lost in the world, to need a friend on these islands. Henry's son, Pueo, was the opposite. Henry had raised him to always know where he was. To watch, to track, to understand his place.

At first Billy stood to the side of the imu and watched as Henry and Pueo carried large, smooth sea stones up from the beach. Henry didn't say anything to either of them. But after the first two trips down to the beach, Pueo called to Billy. "Like help or what?"

Billy ran after Pueo, and then the two of them carried the stones. Pueo showed Billy how to select stones with a large enough diameter, plenty thick, and to pile them on the tarp beside the imu to dry. All this Henry had taught Pueo the day before, and he was proud of the way his son remembered the details, like how to spread the rocks in the sun and turn them to guarantee they were dry because a wet rock could shatter in the fire.

After the stones were gathered, the boys piled kindling sticks in the center of the lua, the pit, and then stacked larger pieces of wood around the edges. While the boys were occupied, Henry went to his neighbors homes and invited them to cook in the pit, too, to bring their slaughtered chickens and goats, their sweet potatoes and taro, and place it all in the oven. When Henry returned to his own yard, the boys were in the water. They had left their shirts in a pile beside the sunning rocks and raced each other to the ocean's edge, to chase the waves and forget for a little while their duties.

Henry stacked the rocks by himself, carefully positioning them on the larger pieces of wood, and studying each rock to be sure it was thoroughly dried. He lit the kindling, then stepped out of the pit. When the kindling caught, he added more wood and a few more stones, and then he went inside the house to prepare the pig.

The boys joined him later. Henry had split several banana stumps with a hatchet, but he showed the boys how to take a rock and pound on the slices of stump. "Break `em up," Henry told them, "Like get da moisture." The boys worked hard, focused on slamming their rocks against the stalk fibers, watching the slices fray and open. Henry worried about them smashing their fingers if they worked too fast, but then he figured pain was a kind of lesson, too, and one they were old enough to learn from.

Just as the sun set behind Haleakalā, the last stones in the imu turned white, and Henry knew the oven was ready to be filled. First he laid the pounded banana stumps over the rocks, spreading them evenly, like a mat or carpet. Next came the ti leaves, which Ellen and Mele had carefully cleaned. The pig came after, in the center of the oven, hot stones tucked under its armpits and neck, and inside the stomach cavity. Pueo and Billy ran to tell the neighbors it was time. Several brought chickens. One had a lamb leg he had purchased at the grocery while a couple others promised they would bring fish in the morning. Henry covered the imu with banana leaves and a tarp. Billy and Pueo wanted to stay up all night and watch the imu, but Ellen wouldn't let them because she knew that if they did they'd be tired and difficult to manage in the morning. Still, Henry was a little sorry when she sent Billy home and Pueo to bed.

He slept beside the imu. He didn't need to but but he liked to, and in the middle of the night, Henry awoke and added the sweet potato, taro and breadfruit, which didn't take as long to bake, and several wet burlap bags to help with the steaming.

The next afternoon, when all the guests arrived for the wedding, Henry carved the pig, offering the richest meat to the bride and groom and their parents. His hands glistened with fat, the oils running between his fingers and over the bump of his wrist bone, and still he kept carving pieces of the pig and offering them to guests.

Pueo and Billy and the other boys played a game of chase. They thread through the crowd, past the aunties seated on fold-out chairs fanning themselves, and around the uncles who chomped on boiled peanuts, noisily sucking the salted juice from the shells. An aunty told the boys to go chase each other back to the banana trees, and so the children scattered from the cement patio where the party was being held. Beyond the banana grove was an expanse of grass, and here the lithe bodies darted back and forth like fish in a sea of green. But after a time, they circled back. One plucked a slice of sashimi with his fingers, another stole a piece of butter mochi from the desert table. "Eh, boy, get outta hea!" an uncle hollered.

Henry handed a piece of the pig's cheek to Mele. Gingerly she gripped it between her fingers and then sucked it into her mouth. The meat was tender, redolent of the earth. She held out her fingers for more. Henry set down his carving knife and rolled his head from side to side, stretching his neck. He licked one of his fingers and winked at her. "Good, yeah?"

Somewhere behind them a cup fell to the ground and liquid splashed—water or beer or POG?—and Ellen's voice rang out, "Get lickins, you." The boys drew together, the whole lot of them rushing for the banana grove again. Henry reached out his hand, fast as an eel, and Pueo was suddenly caught, his forearm in Henry's tight grip. He looked hard at his son. "Aunty told you no run hea." Henry turned Pueo over on his lap, so the boy's ʻokole was in the air, and then Henry slapped his son's legs hard three times. He waited a moment, watched as the skin turned red, the red glistening with pork fat. Then he turned Pueo upright. The boy had tears in his eyes but Henry ignored them. He had to teach Pueo how to listen, how to obey, how to be in the world. He pointed to the banana trees where the other boys had escaped, and Pueo walked in their direction.

Lily asked all the single women to gather because the bouquet had to be thrown, and on the radio the Cowboys made a touchdown. Why does Henry remember this after all these years? The sound of the announcer's voice, tinny on the portable, and the other men cheering as the call was made. In the kitchen, Jeanne, the mother of the bride, cried softly in Ellen's arms, and Ellen shooed Mele away, her own eyes bright with tears to see Mele so young. In the banana grove Billy stopped counting backwards from fifty and regarded Pueo. Billy looked sorry. He craned his neck to see the back of Pueo's legs. Henry wanted to tell the hānai boy that it was nothing, any of the other fathers would have done the same.

"Ready or not," Pueo yelled because Billy had no more words, not even for counting. But then, and suddenly the two of them were running, the chase commenced, their bodies lost to the trees.

Later, the older cousins and their friends gathered for

photographs, and all the young men flashed shakas and all the girls giggled, their breasts shaking in their strapless dresses. Henry washed his hands in the kitchen sink. He took an old toothbrush and scrubbed each cuticle, beneath each nail. Then he went into his and Ellen's bedroom and retrieved his Nikon.

In those days, everyone had disposable cameras or those small plastic point-and-shoots that came in neon colors. But Henry was different. He had this Nikon, big and gray and heavy with machinery. The bridal party had to hold still while Henry focused the lens and tested the lighting, but then photography became something with weight, like painting a portrait, and the girls stopped giggling and looked very serious, and the men linked arms rather than throw shakas, and they all looked older and ready for the world.

Henry called for Pueo, but his son was too far away. Instead, Mele answered. "Have to be strong now, okay?" Henry told her. "Can't drop it." She flexed her biceps to show she was grown enough to hold the prized camera.

He kneeled beside his daughter, looped the strap around her slender neck, and let the heavy camera drop satisfyingly into her hands. He showed her how the shutter speed could be slowed and the aperture widened. How light might be caught. How two boys chasing each other could be glimpsed in motion, their feet and legs and arms blurred like bodies in rain, and how if she balanced the camera on a chair or table, she might capture precise details: a beetle on a leaf or Ellen's face in profile or Pueo's bare feet dangling from a tree branch. And Mele, a quick learner, soon turned the camera on Henry, focused the lens, and captured a pair of hands—swollen, patient, waiting for the rest of the night to unfold.

The Recruit
By K.M. Harris

I hold her journal close to my chest with tears streaming down my face.

Flowing, my tears flow, cascading like narrow rivers down my cheeks. Starting at my blank and emotionless eyes, they run long and dry, ending at my rigid and bitten jaw. Surrendering, my heart surrenders to the aching stabs inside my chest. The punctures cause my rain to pour, charging the static storm in my head and I am a mess in this weather of 'whether.' Whether I cry or pray, it's not going to bring her back and whether I gamble with the Devil to resurrect her soul, it's still not going to bring her back.

Nothing will bring my sister back, only the convoy of vehicles that travel with us to go get her. Take her back home is what we're going to do and after three days of mourning with the family, we'll lay her to rest and send her on her way to join our ancestors.

Oh hard face, oh pale face, oh sorrowful, pained and blank face, how rapidly you've aged since hearing the news of her death. Hours of weeping have claimed the health in your cheeks and moments of remembering her smile crush the jewels in your memory treasure chest. Is this what a mourning face for today's morning face looks like?

Fuck you pain and sorrow and fuck this mourning weather too...

The military base is everything I imagined it to be. Soldiers march in a platoon, ranks of them walking simultaneously to a quick cadence shouted by an angry barker, "Ett, 'ight, 'ett, 'ight, 'ett, 'ight a-a-a-r-r-rt!" Their backs as straight as iron boards, arms swinging shoulder height from front to rear with fisted hands, they march like a group of uniform pressed perfection projecting a feeling of intimidating force and power. Their body language is easy to read too; *don't fuck with us* it says and they dance the regimental 'two-step shuffle' to the sound of, "'ett, 'ight a-a-a-r-r-rt!" The Platoon Sergeant singled out to the side swings his drill cane with a fierce look on his face. Driving past he stares directly at me, his eyes drilling fear into mine. Following my fatigued and fascinated look, his expression yells, *what are you lookin' at, little Miss?!* Though the car windows are wound up, I can still hear him yell "And don't look anywhere else but forward fuck ya! 'Ett, 'ight a-a-a-r-r-rt!" A shock of adrenaline shoots straight to my shoulders. Well, that stopped the crying, didn't it?

The base's speed limit for vehicles is 30km/hr and our car feels so snail like. Poor Dad, I have no idea how he managed to drive eight hours to Kahui Military Base to uplift his daughters corpse. He didn't show his rain on the way down and definitely didn't show his weather patterns either. Instead, the conditions seemed like an overcast day in his world, perhaps it was the clam before the storm. Slowing down even more he turned to Mum to ask, "Is this the one dear? You reckon this is the place?"

"I think so, Dad. That's what the guard at the gate said anyway. See?" she replied showing him the scribble on the piece of paper.

"Oh, okay, well you both wait here and I'll go inside. Or do you wanna come in Mum?"

"Yeah I'll come in. Bubba, you wanna come in with us?"

No response. I don't wanna talk, I just want my sister. *Hurry up and go get her man gee-e-e....*

"Um, well, we'll leave the radio on for you then. We won't be long."

Go, fucken hell! Just go!

Slam! Slam! The car doors shout as Mum and Dad exit the car.

I look down at Elizabeth's journal. The security guard at the gate gave it to Dad on our arrival after saying her Platoon Sergeant wanted us to take it before going in. I touch where she wrote her Army name on the cover; H301206 Officer Cadet E.S Laurent.

Opening the book I see the first page dated 27 January 2002, and on the first line she wrote, "I really don't want to be here anymore. I want to go home."

***

I really don't want to be here anymore. I want to go home.

The bus ride down was horrible but boy was I glad to have brought my discman and CD's! They saved me from listening to everyone else yelling and yahoo'ing on the bus but unfortunately, it didn't save me from the questioning thoughts that plagued my thinking space. Enlisting into the Army seemed like a great idea six months ago but I don't think it's a good idea anymore. I really miss the fam bamz terribly and I miss my boyfriend heaps too...oh hell do I miss you babe. Yep, I think I made a mistake, without a doubt, I really think I have.

The bus pulled up on the parade ground and everyone fell dead silent. No more yelling, no more yahoo'ing, just silence, the awkward, fearful kind. It was as if we were anticipating Jesus's coming, the Armageddon, the end of the world per se or the world as we knew it anyway. Boy was that silence uncomfortable. Unforgettable....

An angry looking man walked on the bus looking like God's creation on a bad day. He had the grumpiest look I had ever seen in my life and boy, did I feel afraid. With his drill cane under his armpit, he eyeballed each and every one of us slowly, taking his sweet time as if to say, 'You're mine now, beetches!' My God did his shoulders rise and fall as I sat there waiting for flames to fly out of his mouth, ready to burn us to smithereens. The thought of that made me clutch my seat in fear...uh oh!!! I need to go to the toilet to take a nervous shit!!!

Boy did he take his time looking at us, and he didn't need words to make us scared either; his intense stare was more than enough. But then he spoke; God's bad-mood-of-a-creation spoke and the words that poured out of his mouth roared like a bellowing volcano. 'Welcome to Kahui Military Camp, my name is Sergeant Dinsdale. You will all call me Sergeant and don't you call me nothing else. From here, I want you to form up outside in one long line facing that building. If you fuck that up, I'll fuck you up. You're in *my* Army now maggots, and your basic training started 2 minutes ago. So get the fuck off my bus and MOVE!'

It's now midnight and everyone has to put an entry into these gay journals. What a gay idea. I mean, what's going to be so different today as to what I write in it tomorrow? Nothings going to change and every day's going to be something along the lines of miles of running, tonnes of press-ups and polishing boots. This is SOOO gay and I hate it already.

They were wankers to us tonight, too. We stood outside in the freezing cold like tin soldier statues waiting to get sized up in uniform. The golden rule around here is 'do NOT look anyone in the eye!!!! If anyone addresses you, you look above their heads and nowhere else!!' One of the gayest rules I've ever heard of but we're 'apparently' not worthy enough to look them. Just because we've got no standards and no skills to offer to the Green Machine family, they've ranked us lower than dog shit. So if we want respect, we have to earn it by working hard. 'Do as you're told,' they told us, 'use your ears and work together not only as a team, but as a family because this is your new family now.'

Pretty fucked up family if you ask me. This is a huge mistake. God, I made a huge mistake. Please let me go home, I wanna go home now.

***

I knew joining the Army would be tough on Elizabeth but enlisting was what she wanted to do. Her sudden passing was a shock to us all because we had high hopes and dreams for her but they're all dead now; they're dead just like how she is ...*oh my sissy, how I miss you terribly....*

Flipping the page, her thoughts continued....

***

What the hell time do you call the crack of dawn? I expected a 5 am wake up for sure, but 3am??!!! Seriously? Like really?

Man, I'm sure I only slept a blink, it was only midnight when I wrote my last entry and 3 hours after that, the next day started!!! It's only day 2 and I'm broken already. I don't know if I'm going to last 10 months of this....

I can't remember much of today's activities but I do recall lots of running, press-ups, running and more press-ups. On top of that was a lot of shouting and mind fucking where they put us in forced stress positions for punishments. Holding a press-up in the lowered position for 30 seconds at a time after doing 20 of them before hand was an easy one...how on earth do they come up with these whack exercises?

There weren't any breaks today either and though I can't stand smoking, I did feel sorry for the smokers. We were all dying from the pain of today's physical infliction but the smokers looked like they were suffering physical and mental crucifixion.

The change in altitude thrashed my lungs every time we were made to run and I had the taste of blood or rusty steel in the walls of my throat. My chest felt so tight and compressed but I faked the actual pain I was feeling. I didn't cry today and that was a huge achievement but boy did I ever want to. I had no fluid in my body to produce tears because I saved it all up to keep myself hydrated. I didn't know when our next meal or drink was going to be and I wasn't prepared to waste any energy on anything that didn't help me get through one more minute of my day. I was determined to get to my bed and now I'm finally in it. The time is now midnight and I'm at the finish line of day two. I know we'll get fed and watered in seven hours time so I'm going to have my cry now; now I'm going to let it all out. Those tears I saved up earlier are all ready to saturate my pillow...

Oh how I miss my family and my babes. I want to go home.

***

Shucks, she sure did a lot of running and press-ups in that first week. Reading her entries made my shoulders feel sore from all the press-ups she had to do. *My poor sissy.* She made me feel so proud though, such a tough biscuit she was. Week one down and she made it through. *Good girl, my sissy. Good girl....*

I didn't think I'd be here today. This time last week I was on the bus thinking that this time this week, I'll be back home. But no, I'm still here. I'm still here.........

Last week was the easiest week. It was full of running, press-ups, yelling, swearing, belittling and all that good stuff they show on movies. I think it was a big scare tactic to be honest because it's still happening but I'm actually used to it. I'm at the point where I'm thinking 'surely, surely you've got some newer tricks guys—cooome on!!!'

My lungs aren't feeling the burn of the altitude change that much and I'm handling the discipline runs heaps better too. I've made some friends but have grown close to one of the girls who said she sat next to me on the bus. She said she wanted to talk to me but was too shy to say anything because I had my headphones on. I told her she should've shoved me or tried to get my attention at least, but shit happens, and at least we're talking now. Leah Pines is her name and she's from a small place somewhere in the middle of the North Island. A real sweetheart of a chick and I think her and I are going to get along just fine.

8 females and 25 males make up the enlisted potentials of this Officer Cadet Basic Training. We sleep separate to the males in a 10 man dormitory room where five single beds line one side of the room and five single beds mirror the exact same arrangement on the other side. Each bed-space has a tallboy cupboard and a small eight-drawer lowboy that stands next to it. Everything has to be folded perfectly in our drawers too, everything right down to our undies, bras and socks.

We're taught to fold our socks so they have 'smiles' on them and they have to be placed standing erect with the crease of the smile-fold facing upwards.

'The objective is for the socks to be smiling team, no sad faces allowed in these drawers,' Sergeant Dinsdale told us. 'You put sad faces in my drawers, I'll put a sad face on your smug mug, do you understand me?!'

'YES SERGEANT!' we all screamed back.

Even down to damn fucking socks, everything has to be perfect. OTT over-the-top attention to detail if you ask me.

We're allowed one photo frame on our drawer thank God, but they've told us it's to remind us that the people in that photo frame are a pretentious group of civilians who claim to care about us. 'They don't CARE about you you maggots' Sarge cooed, 'if they really cared about you, they'd be here in a heartbeat to get you. But no, they leave you here with us, in the country's best care facility. Learn to know who gives a fuck about you and who doesn't maggots because looking out for one another is a big thing in the Green Machine Family.'

I've decided that I'm going to write as much as I can about this place so people believe me when I say they mind fuck us to the core here. They strip away all our feelings and emotions and I fear I'm going to return home acting like a robot. In case that happens, it's their doing, not mine, and this journal is proof.

One of the girls is a foster kid from Mitchelltown, Officer Cadet Wrigley, but we all call her Wriggles. Sergeant Dinsdale ripped her head off today because she didn't have any photos to fill her photo frame so he told her she had five minutes to find a picture of Jesus. 'You can adore His mug on your drawer maggot, adore it 'cos even He doesn't give a fuck about you.'

Sergeant Dinsdales words made me rage. How fucking splenetic can a person be? To add further insult to injury, he told her if she didn't have a picture in 5 minutes, he was going to thrash us all so we all scarped it as fast as we could to find a picture of the Lord. His voice bellowed '4 minutes' down the corridor scaring us all into a panicking frenzy. Luckily, Officer Cadet de la Cruz saved the day by drawing a smiley face with a halo above it on a piece of paper she had ripped out of her journal. She wrote Jesus' name underneath the picture and handed it to Wriggles. We made the five-minute cut off just in time and stood to attention at our bed spaces with 10 seconds to spare. We knew we trumped Sergeant Dinsdale at his own game and smiled on the inside knowing 'we finally got him'...but we were wrong. We were so wrong that we wondered if it was better to have failed than to have succeeded because our short-lived victory became the wine in his goblet. He drank to his triumph by making our pain his euphoric elixir and commanded us to run half an hours worth of hill sprints to the merry tune of 'and that's what you get for making me happy, maggots!'

Surprise me tomorrow, surprise me. Surprise me and teach me something new....

***

She sure did get fucked around a lot the poor thing. I doubt she exaggerated anything too, especially the punishments that were dished out. Come to think of it—

"You okay, Bubba?"

"Yeah, I'm okay, Mum," I replied half smiling. "Gee, that was quick. You guys were quick in there."

"Quick? We've been in there for three hours, babe."

"Three hours?! Who-o-oa!"

Dad started the car and turned the heater on full blast. Not only did time pass by quickly but so did my senses; I didn't realize how cold it was until Dad cranked up the heater.

"We have to stay here for the night babe," Mum said while pulling her seat belt on, "but one night could turn into a few days because of the snow. Road closures are likely to happen so we may have to hold her funeral here. They've given us the option to bury her here too, but we'll see what happens tomorrow. For now, we're all going to be accommodated at the base *Marae.*"

"Do they have a Marae here Mum?"

"Yes they do. They have a carved meeting house, a fully equipped kitchen and dining room complete with separate male and female toilets and showers, so it's like any other Marae in New Zealand—except it's the Army one. We're headed there now so have your working hands ready for dishes and teapots girl 'cos you'll be working that kitchen tonight."

"There's plenty of family here with us, Mum. There'll be heaps of hands for dishes and cups of tea."

I needed to read one more entry before we got to the Marae. Last thing I read she was she wrote something about some friends she had made....

***

It's now week four and I've been here for a month. I don't want to go home now but I'm only partially happy to be here too. Five people have already dropped out and two of them were females. They were weak as fuck anyway, and we all knew they weren't gunna make it.

There's a guy I've become REAL good friends with and he's from the South Island. Bit of a farm boy character and loves his rugby too; said he got a scholarship to go to the Rugby Academy in Gracen. The nearby Army camp made him curious to choose the military as a career and said the only reason why he joined was 'cos he could still play rugby in the Army. Ayrton Carroll is his name and he's a bit of a handsome chap but not my type at all. Definitely brother material but nothing more than that.

There is however, a guy I've taken a fancy to but it's more or less TABOO to think anything could ever happen between us. What's attracted me to him is 'him'; I've never known a man like him before. I feel so guilty for feeling this way though because I have a boyfriend and though I do truly love him, I feel like my love has changed too. Or do I love him? And is it my love that's changed or have I changed? I know I'm not the same Elizabeth anymore, that's for sure. Hell, I haven't even heard my real name since I left home. Instead, I'm addressed as Renty here because people keep saying 'law-rent' instead of 'law-rohn'. I like it anyway. Renty sounds real catchy and affectionate.

I've only told Leah about 'this guy' and she thinks I'm outta my mind crazy. We code-name him 'Jesus' because he's untouchable to the lowly kind. After weeks of getting to know him better, I 'see' him and notice things that no-one else seems to notice...and I get the impression he knows that I notice him too....

Oh.

My.

Gosh.

There's a 'crush' in the picture, she has a *crush*! I *knew* it! And we're at the Marae now too, dammit! I really want to read more....

"Hey Mum, hey um...can I come inside later? I don't feel too well, ay."

"Well no, you have to come in now Bubba. Come on, we're all grieving for Elizabeth and it's time to—"

"Dear, let her stay in the car, ay," Dad chimed in. "It's alright, everyone grieves differently and she said she'll come in. That's the main thing ay, she said she'll come in. But let her come in when she's ready, don't force her otherwise it's only going to make it worse for us when we get home."

You're the man, Dad!

"Hmm, alright then," Mum said, twisting her body round to look at me, "but don't be here all afternoon. Like I said before: dishes and teapots, they don't get done by 'Mister Nobody' and you need to represent your sister just like she represented us. So take as much time as you need but remember, we need your hands in the kitchen too."

"Thank you, Mumma. I love you." Leaning forward to kiss Dad, I whispered, "And I love you too, Daddy."

***

We're on the parade ground today learning drill. More movements, more foot work and correcting of—

Bo-o-oring, I don't want to read about tha-a-at...hm-m-m......ah ha! Here we go....

Leah told me a secret today. She said she's found a 'Jesus' just like me!!! It's Ayrton, she likes Ayrton and I told her to GO FOR IT!!! I wonder if he likes her though, he doesn't seem to show it the weirdo lol. Anyway, I told him about Jesus and he said to forget about it 'cos I'll end up getting crucified like the REAL Jesus if anything ever happened. 'Renty.' he said. 'be careful about liking Jesus girl. Us lads heard Jesus talking with his boys the other night and they talk about you girls ay. They talk about which one of you is the hottest and from the sound of their voices, I think Jesus likes you too. But don't go there girl, don't go there 'cos you know the rules: no fraternization, period. If you get caught, you'll get the boot for sure. Stay focused my mate, stay in the game but don't be a player.'

Ayrton was right and I love how he always looks out for me, we really do have each others back. From here on in, I'm staying focused. Focused and nothing else. Promise....

Yeah, right! I bet she *didn't*!

We had our fitness test today, a timed run, press-ups and sit-ups. Females have 12 minutes and 20 seconds to complete the run in so the punishment sprints and running paid off today because I aced the 2.4 kilometres in 10 minutes and 40 seconds. As for the press-up punishments, they paid off too and I'm so thankful that Jesus beasted us with press-ups everyday because that really....

Oh hold up...oh man. Um-m-m...I hope no-one reads this or they'll 'get' who Jesus is. Shit....

Wha-a-at?! Jesus made them do sprints and press-ups and...hold on...Jesus....Jesus had to be one of the Sergeants!

Who-o-oa...I wonder if it was that—

"Squ-u-uad—halt!"

And just like that, I saw the angry barker from earlier in the day. You've got to be joking I thought. What the hell is *he* doing here. *Just because this is your Army base, doesn't mean you can invite yourself to the Marae too.* Well hang on, it *is* his Marae, so what am I on about? Hm-m-m, I better get in the kitchen. I think I can hear the teapot calling.

***

"You're washing. Bubba"

"No, I'm not, you are," I told my younger cousin in a condescending tone. "I've done my time doing dishes mate, it's your turn to take on the ill-fated apprenticeship of doing dishes, and don't moan about it either—it's life and it happens. You'll get over it and you'll turn 17 one day too, just like me and then you can boss other young ones around to do the dishes that you won't have to do."

"Fa-a-ar I was just saying man, I can't do all these dishes by myself! You're a stink cousin, Bubba. I'm telling your Mum on you."

"Do you see the sympathy in my face? Cuz the care factor reads zero ay so run along now and don't bother me about dishes. I'm not in the—"

Whoa....

Angry Barker at one o'clock. What a fucking intense piece of work he is. *Why is he looking at me? No, not looking at me, more like staring me the fuck out. How fucking rude.*

I deliberately shoot Angry Barker a 'whatever' frown and roll my eyes. *I ain't one of your soldiers, and you can't intimidate me, weirdo.*

"Miss, excuse me Miss?" a short, young Maori woman in uniform enquired politely.

"Err...kia ora," I replied smiling.

"Kia Ora to you, too," she smiled, leaning in for a kiss on the cheek. "I believe you're Officer Cadet Laurent's little sister?"

"Yes, yes I am. And you said Laurent correctly too! I'm used to hearing it pronounced as 'law-rent'.'

Chuckling, she replied, "Your sister did school us on how to say it properly but we called her Renty anyway. I'm Leah, one of her close friends—"

"Jesus..."

"Ah, excuse me?"

"Jesus," I said to her with wide eyes. "Jesus."

"Ah-h-h, o-o-oh-ka-a-ay. Jesus. Yes, there is a story about Jesus, but I'm not the one that drew the picture for our friend Wriggles if that's what you mean."

"No, Jesus, Leah. *Jesus*! You know about Jesus!"

Her pupils widened slightly and she swallowed hard. She turned her head slowly to look behind her, and that's when my life changed forever. I looked in the direction she was looking in and saw the most incredibly, handsome man I'd ever laid my eyes on. Call it a stupid teenage girl crush but the soldier I was looking at was over 6 feet tall and draped in the most masculine and muscle-y body I'd ever seen.

Oh. My. Gosh.

"Um, what do you know about Jesus?"

"Sorry...what?"

"Jesus," Leah queried. "What do you know about him?"

"Oh yeah, right! Jesus," I replied, snapping out of my dream. "Um, yeah, I know some stuff but I know you know more. What can you tell me?"

"Officer Cadet Pines, come here now." We both jolted and looked at the Angry Barker.

"Yes, Sergeant!" she replied. "I have to go. I'll try talk to you later."

Fuck you Angry Barker! O-o-oh he was starting to make my blood boil.

"Oh well, I guess I better grab a tea pot then," I sighed, grabbing a box of tea bags.

I watched the water gush from the hot water urn, a steaming waterfall crashing into the pot of bagged tea leaves. People's chatter chorused loudly in the dining room with sounds of intermittent laughter up-beating the conversational tone. Aunties growled at the kids to stop running around in the kitchen in part-time nasal pitches and bustling plates clanged in the kitchen sink from the cuzzies doing the 'mission dish washing.'

My mourning face seemed to have worn off thanks to the content in my sister's journal. I felt I was on a mission to find out who Jesus was and I wanted to know what he knew about Elizabeth's death. In a daydream, I imagined my sister collapsing under the weight of her 30kg pack, gasping for breath, slowly going blue in the face from the lack of oxygen. She lied about her asthma to all of us; to her real family and her Army family. She told Mum and Dad that the Army let her in with her asthma but she told the Army that she didn't even have it. Nobody there knew she had asthma so when she had her asthma attack, so no one knew it was her asthma that caused her to fall. The medical kits they had on them didn't contain inhalers so they weren't able to give her temporary treatment and the help her section commander radioed in arrived far too late for her to be evacuated in time. It was one a.m. when she fell and the first vehicle arrived in their location two hours later— too late. *Oh no, I can feel the static storm forming in my head again and tears are starting to bruise the ducts in my eyes....*

"Excuse me, Miss, I'm just going to turn the water off," a voice said beside me.

"What?" I replied in a daze.

Oh my God! It was him*!*

We both stood there locked in a stare. His eyes were perfect, a dark chocolate brown color and his long black eyelashes blinked at me in amazement. He had fair skin but didn't look completely European; half Maori at least and half something else for sure. But that was the least of my worries; he was just so damn handsome, so handsome that I couldn't take my eyes off him.

"Um, the waters off now," he said softly, smiling slightly as he stepped back. "I guess I should let you carry on making cups of tea for everyone."

"Errr, yeah, I guess so," I said breathlessly. "I better do these teas then."

"Yeah, I guess so."

"Yeah, yeah, right...okay. Teas! Um, hm-m-m."

I put the lid on the teapot and turned to head into the dining room. He stopped me midway, reaching out to touch my elbow and I looked at him blinking, waiting for him to speak. *Oh, speak to me you stunning specimen....*

"I'm sorry for your loss."

I'm sorry for your loss.... A tear dislodged itself from my eye.

"I'm sorry, Miss. I didn't mean to make you cry."

"It's okay," I said forgivingly. "Sorry, that wasn't supposed to happen." I placed the teapot on the bench and reached into my pocket for a tissue. "Excuse me, I just need to blow my nose."

"No worries, I won't hold you up too much longer. I just wanted to give you my condolences in person. I believe you're Officer Cadet Laurent's sister?"

"Yes, yes I am. I'm Thayer—Thayer Laurent."

"Kia Ora, Thayer. I'm Ayrton—Ayrton Carroll. Your sister will always be one of my best friends, ay. She was a great girl, like a sister to me, actually."

I suddenly looked straight at him, releasing "Jesus" from my mouth.

"Ah, pardon?"

"Jesus," I said to him with wide eyes. "*Jesus*."

He stood back and distanced himself from me, his energy changing like a light switch. He looked down at the ground and tilted his head to the left and right quickly, coughing nervously before squaring me in the eyes with a serious look. His shoulders rose and fell as he bit his lip apprehensively and the unexpected tension between us heightened.

"Look, I only knew about them getting serious with one another in the last two months before her death. They did well at keeping their relationship a secret because Leah and I protected your sister from the others finding out. Renty snuck out at ungodly hours of the morning to be with him and I have no idea how she found the energy to keep up with us during the day when she visited him during the night. She was starting to fall in love with him, Thayer. Madly, truly, and deeply, and since her passing, he hasn't been the same. He wasn't with us when she had her attack but—"

"Babe, we have to go. We've got two minutes to form up outside. Sarge just gave the order."

Babe?

Ayrton looked at me and looked at Leah. Leah looked at Ayrton and looked at me. I looked at Leah and looked at Ayrton. We stood in what looked like the Bermuda 'Looking' Triangle.

"Babe, don't be late, please. I have to go look for the others."

"Okay, I'll be there."

"Is...is Leah your girlfriend?" I said.

"Yeah, well, sort of," he replied. "It's complicated." His eyes seemed to be disappointed and I returned his look with disbelief. "I have to go, Thayer."

I frowned, overwhelmed by the mixed thoughts flooding my emotions. "Wait, Ayrton wait, please." Grabbing his hand I looked into his eyes searching. "Can I write to you?"

Ayrton smiled, his eyes sparkling slightly. "I'd love it if you did."

"Cool. I will and I hope you don't mind me asking you more about Jesus too."

"You won't be asking him nothing about Jesus, Miss." Ayrton and I jolted, reacting to the tone of the Angry Barker.

"Get outside and form up Carroll.'

"Yes, Sergeant Dinsdale!" Ayrton replied with immediate obedience. He didn't say goodbye to me and didn't look back either. Instead, like a pre-programmed robot, he sprung into action to the tune of the Angry Barkers hypnotic command.

"Hey Mister, hang on a minute," I said to Sergeant Dinsdale, annoyed. "My sister has just passed away and we're grieving right now and so are her friends. I'd appreciate it if—"

"You're grieving?" he said, drilling his questioning eyes into mine. "Excuse me Miss, but *you're* grieving?" The intensity in his eyes started to freak me out.

He continued. "Forgive me for not passing on my condolences, but it's because I'm grieving too. Read her journal a bit more Miss Thayer, it's why I gave it to the security guys at the gate. When Officer Cadet Laurent passed away, I went straight to her room to retrieve her journal and lucky I did, too. It has some very personal information in it that the Military Police do not need to be aware of. Hopefully, by reading her journal, you'll not only understand what she went through, but what we're all going through now. So yes, I understand you and your family are grieving but we're grieving too Miss Thayer—we're grieving, too. I didn't just lose an Officer Cadet, I lost a beautiful woman who I began to fall in love with and one that was carrying our child. Losing her was enormous, but losing her when she was eight weeks pregnant with our baby was something else. It's true that she had an asthma attack, but her body became stronger during Officer Cadet Training too, so she would've survived it. The stress of the pregnancy took a toll on her though and unfortunately, the asthma attack was too strong for her. Without the aid of an inhaler, she couldn't fight it as long as she probably could've if she wasn't pregnant, so we lost her...and here we are now. So don't bother Officer Cadet Carroll with letters about Jesus, alright? Because I'm Jesus. I'm the Jesus she wrote about. Given the fact that what I've just told you isn't the 'Good News', at least you can say that what I've just said is the truth."

I felt like dropping dead to the floor.

The destiny of these chosen officer cadets is to lead a group of people that descend from the Maori God of War, Tumatauenga. They train to the point of exhaustion, strengthen their minds to capacity's brink and wake up to do it all over again each and every day because they love the Army they joined.

There is no task that these officers and soldiers cannot do and there is no mission that this band of men and women will not complete without giving it guts and glory.

This is Tumatauenga's tribe. This is Tumatauenga's elite collective. This is the physical manifestation of Tumatauenga's legacy.

And though I am unable to continue walking alongside my Green Machine family in the world of the living, I am still a part of them through the spirit-child that connects me to a man that once taught me and loved me. His destiny is to continue imparting his experience and knowledge onto the future leaders of Tumatauenga's people until his path joins mine in the spirit realm. Until then, we will wait for him here while he carries out the dreams and purpose patterns his ancestors envisioned for his life journey.

As for my sister Thayer, this is only the start of her blazing legacy. A spark of passion has found it's place in her heart, not only for carrying on what I never could, but for the man that captured her breath and stole her smile...her story continues....

Eagle Breath
By Ellen van Neerven

CJ Court is on his way back home with the bread and cheese. He drives down the main road, seeing Baga-bagah pressed by the midday sun in front between the gaps of the buildings. He reaches his part of town—the groups of small houses like his. Could be the cheapest housing in Queensland. A lot of his mob lived in these houses—here was the biggest Aboriginal population outside the city. Between the houses weaved dirt bike paths—the ground system—tracks going to the main road and to the park. He sees the glint of Aunty Louise's red scooter moving through.

When he spots young ones he slows and keeps an eye out for his kids but there's no kid he recognizes. Not even at the park, on the bike hills and play set. Days like this his kids take their bikes out and roam wild. It's the way things should be, though he wants to catch them to remind them about being home for lunch, it wouldn't eat itself.

He sees his house coming up and now Baga-bagah is in full view. It didn't get old — the way the clouds came up and made a scarf around the mountain. On the left was the clearing to the creek named after his grandmother and on the right was the ancestral cemetery hill where a lot of their mob were buried. Flat open land. Dry.

Swallowing, he parks by the house and walks out into his land. The house needs work, he's always reminded about it when he sees it like this. The teal paint wearing off. He has a moment of quiet, looking up into the arches, before the goats, the dogs charge him. He plays with the puppy but ignores the rest for now. They didn't get fed last night and he doesn't want to look at them.

He had woken with possibility when the dawn skipped in. Might have had a smile on his face. He'd start on Monday. The job had come at just the right time. It was a traineeship, insulting as his age, and far from the most money he'd made in his life, but it was doing something good, this program, they were building something. It was for men who had been unemployed for a while. He didn't think anyone would give him a chance anymore. The job was with the local council, working on his own country, building the nature trail at Baga-bagah, the rocky steps down the mountain. He's made his mind up he's ready to be a new man, to be who he used to be.

He goes through the front door, calls out to Hannah, drops the bread and cheese on the bench. The bread's from the German baker in town and the cheese's from the co-up, made in Nimbin, Bundjalung cheese. On the table are stacks of silver coins as high as the loaf of bread. CJ tried to make bread for a while but the kids wouldn't eat it. Wouldn't go near it. And there were other things he should be useful at.

He wants to make a special lunch for his family—proper egg sandwiches, like he used to. He used to make lunch every Saturday when he was working during the week.

He goes out and through the shrub path, the dogs following him, into the vegetable garden. He gets some herbs, beetroot, bush tomatoes, baby cucumbers. He walks out to the chicken coup to get some eggs for the salad. Hannah's there. She's often with the animals.

"Hi darlin'," he says in a sing-song voice. "I'm back."

"Hey, CJ," she seems a little distracted. "Did you get the stuff for tea?"

He slaps his jeans, "No, forgot, sorry."

She sighs. "It's okay, I just…"

"What's wrong?" he said, moving closer.

She points at the chooks, and he realizes there's one missing. There was a trace of feathers on the ground but no bird. He knows instinctively it must have been an eagle—instead of a fox, one of the dogs, or a python. There was no way they could get in, he made it foolproof after years of trial and error.

"CJ, you said you were going to do a roof. When?"

He touches her shoulder, "It's okay." She's upset—but he's strangely exhilarated. The eagle has paid him a visit. He wonders what he did to deserve it.

He walked into the coup, the chickens scattered. He bent over and touched the discarded feathers, not knowing what he'd get out of them. Hannah was watching him. He gave her a smile, and picked up some eggs from the coup. He put two in his pockets, and passed the rest to her to put in the basket, weaved by her Bapu Islander grandmother.

"What were you going to make for tea? I can go back to the shops later," he said.

"I was... It doesn't matter. Max had her doubts about it this morning."

"Tell me how two blackfellas raised children whose fav food is store-bought macaroni cheese?" CJ shook his head.

Hannah made a little expression. "I know." She gave him the basket. "We'll just get some fish from Robbie. They always come around after lunch with their catch from the Logan River."

CJ nods. He doesn't think it's much point to say that the young fellas haven't come around in a while, maybe a year.

"I'll get started on lunch. You come up when you're ready, okay?" He kisses her cheek. He adds, as an afterthought. "I'm sorry about the old girl. She had a good life."

***

He remembers the eagle feather in her hat. He had met her at a bbq on Lee Fisher's property. Had all of his teeth then, wearing a big red check shirt and a puffer vest. Jeans that hadn't been washed since he took them from his bigger brother's caravan floor. Everyone in town there, nearly. Getting grogged up. The horses are watching from the fence. Someone calls a dance, here they do their own version. The loose, sleazy version. The boys get to grab that girl real tight. She has her hands on your hair sometimes. That vertebra deep in your neck that always hurt CJ after a day on and off the tractor. Well all his body hurt. When he got home he'd play up, croon to the goats, "No I ain't gonna work on Maggie's Farm no more."

He was yelling this out with Lee Fisher and a few of them, his mouth wide open, relaxing into this shout, all the while looking over at Hannah. She was wearing a scruffed denim jacket, and jeans too. A cowboy hat, like one he used to own. His favorite, even if he had two more since. Blackfellas maybe don't wear cowboy hats much but he liked it and he saw she did too.

He once saved an eagle chick from rock-throwing kids, put it in his hat. He sided over to Hannah at the fence and told her that story, pointed to her hat. She smiled and he took it off her and flipped it up in the air. The heat of the night seemed to flip over when he did that and they watched it fall back into his hands. He felt sweat had gathered under his arms. She took the hat back off him a little roughly. Another round of dancing started around them and he wordlessly pointed and she grabbed his hands. He nodded his head to the music, gargled nothing, his throat limp, looked at her hair on her neck. He moved his hands cautiously to her waist.

"Hey," she said, suddenly moving away. She looked down.

"What?" he said.

Her toe ring. Vanished in the sand. He was on his hands and knees looking for it. A few minutes of this while the dances went on around him and she giggled and then his brother, Alex's voice thundered in.

"She's gammon with you, bro."

He got up quickly and saw her amused face and kissed her, his tongue keen. He heard his brother behind him laugh with surprise but he noticed nothing else after that as she put her hand on the back of his head, just there.

***

He put the eggs under water in an almost dead saucepan, blackened from Max trying to heat up some chicken soup while they weren't home. Humming to himself while he washed the vegetables, he smiled in surprise, he hasn't heard his hum for a while.

He walks around the house, cleaning up the kids' morning warpath as he goes. The most important thing about a house, he reckons, was how it held the light. The July light comes through the living room, the faint edges of the range. He moves down the hallway, sliding his socks down the wooden floorboards. More strange noises. The way the house hisses you'd think someone'd put hot water down the sides. CJ had the thought to put a skylight, here, in the children's bedroom. There was no way of being outside in this room. And Max and James had nothing but bad luck since daddy lost his job, mummy went womba, grandmummy died, Uncle Alex shot some girl. It was easier to think of these things happening to them than happening to himself.

All those months of having nothing come in—staying up all night until first light, seeing the hills and kids in the morning and worrying even more. Things will change. He's turned it around before.

***

Hannah was a girl from a higher country. Her mob was from up north. Her daddy came here as a cane cutter. They didn't have much between them and Hannah's daddy had less than nothing and took CJ's things, his other pair of jeans and his tea cups and his chainsaw.

They got married in December and after their first night in the house, just the two of them, they were on the road the next day. Family biz.

Max was inside her belly then. He drove through the valley careful. The river had let summer in. They stopped to buy rhubarb jam in the little town near the border. They'd eat it when the baby's born, he said to her. He wished he could give her more. But money was just petrol these days. Hannah said he didn't need to go to family and do these things, but he did. And her family were more demanding, she just didn't see it.

***

He returns to the eggs. He gets a bowl out of the cupboard. When they're good, he rinses them with cold water and peels them clumsily with his calloused stumpy fingers. A burn on his thumb. He mixes the eggs with Hannah's mayo and a spoon or so of her curry powder and tinned pickles. The eggs the eagle had chosen for his family. Then he puts the chopped lettuce and bush tomatoes and beetroot and cucumber in other bowls. He opens a family sized tin of tuna. He is starting to get anxious that he might have made a meal for no one, for nothing, the house is quiet. He is cutting through the bread when Max and James come in, dirty-kneed, and he feels relief fold into the room, their hungry smiling impatient faces, and Hannah behind them, her hair has been washed, he's just realized it. She's been washing her hair. He puts his hands down, gestures for them to grab a plate.

The Maze
By Bill Wetzel

This was the one year of my life when I said *braymer* instead of *brahma*; the time I was kicked in the chest by a bull, nearly killing me.

My girlfriend stayed in her car while I lie prone in a rodeo arena outside of Cut Bank, Montana on the Blackfeet Indian Reservation. Furiously writing. Integrating the world around her, transforming it magically from pen to paper. The paramedics frantically worked on me, trying to prevent cardiac arrest. I was awake the whole time. Coherent, yet unable to move.

They thought I was unconscious.

One paramedic kneeled over me preparing to deliver a jolt of electricity. Rubbing the handles of a defibrillator together. About ready to yell, "Clear!"

"Did I win?" I asked.

The paramedic nearly fainted.

"No," someone out of sight said. "One judge marked you and the other didn't."

Another tenth of a second, I would have won the rodeo. Another tenth of a second, I would have rolled out from underneath that bull. Two-tenths away from health and glory.

Life is not a matter of inches. It is a matter of instances. Moments. Seconds. Tenths of seconds. What we do or do not do in life will be decided by painfully miniscule moments in time. A blink of an eye will determine success or failure.

I was one second from being shocked to death, possibly about to enter cardiac arrest and all I cared about was if I made the ride or not.

Meanwhile, my girlfriend was writing the essay of her life.

Dust was swirling everywhere. The arena was freezing cold. I was loaded into an ambulance on a stretcher, with what I would later find out was a bruised heart.

She appeared out of nowhere, leaned over me and whispered: "I think this is the best thing I have ever written."

***

My evening was spent in the emergency room. Shortly after my arrival, a bear attack victim was brought in from Glacier National Park. The doctor on call walked in, took one look at his two patients, then quipped dryly: "It looks like *Da Bulls* and *Da Bears* won tonight."

I tell that joke now like it was funny at the time.

You could tell the doctor enjoyed being humorous. The type of doctor who liked to keep patients in *stitches*. A real *cut up*. Sometimes people who work in stressful careers have a morbid sense of humor. He dealt with illness all the time. Trauma. Death. He never saw someone who didn't have a complaint. His life was dealing with those in pain.

A month later he treated me again, this time for a dislocated shoulder.

Three months later he was the medic who treated me for another dislocated shoulder and a torn knee ligament at a wrestling tournament. Never once did he stop cracking jokes. Never once did he tell me to do something different with my life.

Guys like me keep people like him in business.

Guys like me reiterate his jokes.

Guys like me sport scars and jokes as if they were Medals of Honor.

They become part of our own mythology. Stories which are true, but not true. Funny, yet not funny. Those moments when I was tough and legendary.

Except I was not.

By then my girlfriend was long gone. She left me for college and another life. One far from an Indian reservation. Where she could write and be intellectually stimulated by men with life prospects and no broken bones.

But that night she paced the emergency waiting room. Scribbling notes. Finishing her essay. She paused only to step outside, smoking cigarettes while talking to the others waiting for their loved ones. Interviewing them. Scorching each detail to memory. Putting them down on paper.

The nature of my injuries required spending the night in the hospital for observation. Without painkillers. I was sleepless. Agitated. Hurting. Sometime in the early morning hours she came to me.

"Read this."

Her flat eyes held all the emotion of a bull.

Or was that a bear?

She wrote about hospitals. Visiting emergency room time after time after time. Every rodeo I was injured at. Every wrestling tournament. All the memories she had. That *we* had. She wondered what was wrong with me. Why would I keep doing this to myself? Sacrificing my body? She salvaged it all. Our life together up to that point.

It was the most amazing work I have ever read.

I never slept more beautifully.

***

This one time we went to a maze, right outside of Kalispell, Montana, on the road back to the Blackfeet Indian Reservation. We had been in Missoula, listening to one of her favorite poets read at the University of Montana. I could not understand any of it. I was a bull rider. An athlete. A dumb farm hick. If I could not fight, wrestle or ride it, it was beyond my comprehension. But I loved her from the first second I saw her.

Working for the summer at Glacier National Park. I would do anything for her.

It didn't matter if I felt out of place or not.

We stopped at this maze. It was wooden and three-dimensional. I had been in it once with my brothers when we were children. It seemed tiny now. Stuffed with people. We held hands throughout. It was scary. Dark from the dwindling evening light. I kept saying the same thing over and over and over.

"Go right, go right, go right."

Every turn was worse. The crowd thickened. I felt like a platelet in a blocked artery. Barely able to move. Holding on to her hand as long as possible. Then, with instant relief, the people surged forward. The path ahead opened in a rush.

We were separated.

"Go right, go right, go right" raced through my mind.

I was out of the maze, turning, smiling, ready to hug and kiss the woman who was a few steps behind me.

She was not there.

I waited outside the maze. Each person coming out was her for an instant. My memory fell back to my pre-driving years. Waiting for one of my friends to drive out to our farm in the country, to pick me up so we could go to town. Every car coming down the dirt road near our house seemed as if it could be a friend. In those times, each car's lights become distinct.

"Oh yeah, Bubba's pickup has one headlight like that!"

Momentary jubilation. Then the vehicle would pass.

I would nearly die from the disappointment each time.

I waited for her. Every person was her. Then not. I could feel my heart bruise again. Sinking. The kid working at the maze would not let me go back in to search for her. I was about to pay and enter through the front of the maze again, when finally she walked out.

I always felt *sauntered* was a better description of how she moved.

This was the second time I saw those flat eyes.

The third was a short time later when she *sauntered* out of my life forever with no explanation.

***

This story is not true. However, like anything I write there is truth in it. What I did was weave different instances in my life together, creating a fictional story. This style, including the revelation I am making now, comes from an Amy Hempel short story titled: *The Harvest.*

For example, I did once wrestle and ride bulls. I also had many injuries because of these activities. One of them occurred at a high school rodeo outside of Cut Bank, Montana, where I was kicked in the chest by a bull, which bruised my heart and also a lung.

The part about the funny doctor and the bear attack victim was accurate.

I had no girlfriend at the time though.

I also was barely spared the indignity of a defibrillator when I asked the paramedic if I had won. Again, one judge marked me and one did not.

The girl with the essay has some truth to it as well. She was in one of my writing classes. She wrote two of the most beautiful essays I have ever read. One was was about memories. In the other, she wrote about taking her sick roommate to an emergency room.

And maybe a part of me had a little artistic crush on her when we first met.

But we never had a romantic relationship.

As for her flat eyes, I only saw those once. Right before she *sauntered* out of my life forever with no explanation.

Then there is the passage asserting life is a matter of instances. I mentioned this because if I would have taken the time to stop her, perhaps things could have ended up differently. However, I let her go. In a matter of a few seconds, I blew it. My failure may have been decided by those few moments.

This is something I will never know.

As for the maze, I had a dream about navigating it with her, precisely as described in the story. I have been in it, as a child, in real life too.

In my dream, we were not coming from a poetry reading. We were giving separate readings of our own work at a fairground next to where the maze was located. This fairgrounds is nonexistent in reality. In my dream, the actress Kirsten Dunst attended my reading with a group of anonymous locals.

After the maze incident, I allowed the girl to cool down, then I went to eat frybread with my new friend, Kirsten Dunst.

Including this in my story would defy all reality, so there was no need for it.

***

The one aspect which hit home for me was correlating my bruised heart injury to the pain of standing outside the maze waiting for her.

Every single day since she walked away, I have felt like I did outside the maze in my dream. Wishing to hear from her. To run into her. To read her beautiful words somewhere. In a newspaper. Magazine. A novel. I would do anything to know her again. But all I can do is wait.

I am forever outside that maze.

Counting seconds.

Instances.

Preparing to seize those next precious moments.

As soon as I see her, Ill say all those things I never said as I watched her walk away. I will not waste another tenth of a second.

I will not allow myself another bruised heart.

You know, nowadays bull riders wear protective vests. When I rode they were not required. This has reduced the number of serious injuries significantly. If I had worn one that day, I may have never been hurt at all. Probably would have only had the wind knocked out of me for a short time.

However, I suspect *Da Bears* are still easily winning their battles with hikers in Glacier National Park.

I Hear My Ancestors Singing

By Kenneth Dyer-Redner

I sit on the steps outside the high school basketball gym. I had just hit a couple of long pull up shots and some free-throws to seal the victory. It was nothing big. On the dirt court outside my HUD house, I spent hours shooting those same shots, those shots that would take me off the reservation. At the bar, my drunk-uncle tells everyone that I'm the next Jim Thorpe. I tell myself it's true, and I believe it.

My dad drives up to the curb. He only comes around when I have a game. I don't care anymore. I love and hate my father equally. I open the door and sit down in the dusty brown Cadillac. It's a real Indian car. The heater doesn't work and the trunk is held together with a bungee cord. My dad looks at me and smiles. "Good game, Son," he says.

I smile. It's a great feeling to be a winner. It's an even better feeling to come from the reservation and win against these non-Indians.

"Yeah, you did alright," he continues. "You turned the ball over a couple times and you need to go to the hole more."

I look out the window. "It's cold outside, huh?"

"What?"

"Nothing," I say.

We drive to the Fallon Paiute-Shoshone Indian Reservation. I get out of the car and tell my dad I'll see him at the next game. He tells me to do those ball-handling drills and shoot more jump-shots. I tell him I'll do them every day. He smiles and leaves in a cloud of dust. I walk in the house and take a shower. I sit down on the couch, eat a bowl of cereal, and wait for my girlfriend to come over.

***

My mom and dad divorced when I was four. He cheated on my mom. When I was twelve I asked her if she hated my dad. She said, "I don't *hate* him. But, I sure in the hell don't *like* him."

When I was fifteen I asked my dad why he cheated on my mom. He said, "Well, she wasn't giving it to me. So I had to get it somewhere."

I didn't want to think about what *it* was.

At nights my mom works at a Casino in town. She makes it to the games when she can. Tonight—like most nights—she's working.

***

My girlfriend knocks on the door. I get up and answer. She walks in and kisses me. She smells of alcohol and smoke. I ask her, "Where were you?"

She says, "I was with Jill. We were just cruising around after the game." She looks at me. "Are you mad?" She leans in close, licks my ear, and whispers, "What can I do to make you happy?"

"You can go brush your teeth," I say.

"Whatever," she says. "I'm gonna leave."

"I'm just joking." I really wasn't. "You know what you can do."

She smiles. She takes my hand and leads me into my bedroom. We have sex.

***

My girlfriend is half white. She lives in town with her brother; her white mom and stepdad. I see her real dad every once in a while. One time I saw him at a gas station in town. He was carrying a gym bag and asked if I could give him a ride to the rez. I told him I had to go to school. He told me he left some house where he was staying about an hour ago. He started confessing his drug addiction and problems. I all ready knew about them. He told me he was going to go to rehab in Washington. I told him that was a good idea. He told me I make all the Indians proud. He said I was almost as good at basketball as my dad. I told him I was better. He laughed.

***

My girlfriend and I lie on the bed. We hold hands. She tells me, "I love you."

I say, "I love you, too." And I mean it. It's dark in the room, so dark that I can barely make out her features. She's quiet. I poke her in the ribs. She usually laughs. She doesn't laugh this time. She grabs my hand and pulls me next to her. I ask her, "What's wrong?"

She says, "I don't want to tell you because I'm afraid you'll get mad."

"I won't get mad."

"You promise?"

"Yeah."

"Say it."

"I promise."

"It's nothing," she says.

"You can't say that and expect me to just forget it."

She turns her back to me. I pull her gently. She doesn't budge. I can hear her sniffling. "Are you crying?"

***

My girlfriend cried a lot. Most of my t-shirts had little black stains on the shoulders. At first I couldn't figure out what the stain was coming from. After a while it dawned on me: m*ascara*. I was constantly consoling her. She cried because of her father. She cried when she drank. She cried when we argued. She was always getting upset while I always tried to make her happy.

***

"Why are you crying?"

"Because I love you."

"Because you love me?"

She turns to look at me, then turns away.

"What's wrong?" I ask.

She lies there and cries quietly. I wait, hoping that she'll tell me what's bothering her. The minutes tick by. She finally mutters something.

"What?"

She pauses for a while, then mumbles something again.

"What the hell are you saying?"

"I'm pregnant. I didn't want to say anything. I don't want you to give up basketball for me."

I wipe the tears off her cheeks. The music gently floats in the air.

***

These past few months I'd started receiving letters from colleges:

Dear Prospective Athlete,

You have been recognized as an exceptional student athlete. Enclosed is a questionnaire. Please fill it out and return it. We will be in contact.

I had letters from nearly every Division I college on the west coast: UCLA, University of Utah, UNR, UNLV, Washington State, Arizona State, Fresno State, Stanford, Cal, Oregon State, University of Washington, Navy, Army, Air Force, Colorado, Colorado State, Oregon State, University of Oregon, Boise State ....

Not bad for an Indian kid from the reservation. My coach told me if I kept playing well, I would start getting calls.

***

She says, "I can get an abortion."

"I don't think that's right."

"Well, what are we going to do?"

"I don't know."

"I don't want you to give up basketball for me."

"Are you sure you're pregnant? I mean did you take a test or see the doctor?"

"Women know these things—they know their bodies. I've been

feeling sick in the mornings and I'm late."

"How late?"

"You don't believe me? I wouldn't just say something like this!" She starts to cry again. "I knew you were going to get mad."

"I'm not mad."

I am mad. I'm mad at myself.

***

She says, "Push on my stomach."

"What?"

"Push on my stomach."

"No. Why?"

She rolls on her back, reaches for my face.

"Push on my stomach."

My heart beats. It sounds like a hand drum. She grabs my hand, and places it on her stomach.

I lay my head on her belly and listen to my unborn baby. I can hear her stomach gurgling. Maybe it's my baby smiling. Maybe it's my baby crying. Maybe it's my baby struggling to live because they know what their mom is going to say.

"Push on my stomach."

I began to cry. I listen for something, anything. I wait. I kiss her stomach. I whisper, "I'm sorry." I sit up and push on her stomach with all my weight. She watches me. I push on her stomach. She cries into a pillow. I push on her stomach. I cry. I push on her stomach.

I turn my back to her and sit on the edge of the bed. A stillness settles—beyond silent.

"What are you thinking?" she asks.

"Nothing," I say.

"You can't think of nothing."

"I can."

"How?"

"It's easy."

"How?"

"I don't know."

I look at my hands and try to make out the shape of them now that things have become so dark.

"I don't want to talk about it," I say. "I don't want to talk to you right now."

She says, "You can be very mean sometimes."

"Yes," I say and put my hands down. "Can't we all?"

I could feel my heart beating. It sounds like a hand drum. It sounds like singing. She says, "Do you love me? Do you love me like you used to?"

I stand up and look at her pleading eyes. "Maybe," I say. "Maybe not."

Jimtown Ruined My Life
Cinnamon Spear

I didn't know the woman on the couch with Dad, but she was ugly. She crossed her legs as easily as she'd just crossed me, and he loved her for it. He loved this woman, more than he loved my mom. In a mere twenty minutes, she had walked into our home and completely wrecked me. She then simply sat back liquor loose and leaned into him comfortably, as if she had spent thirty fucking years next to him. It was disgusting.

I never saw her before that day. He'd left my mother at Bunut and brought this bitch home. I hated her. I hated both of them and the psychotic smirks they wore. He was proud of her. He draped his arm heavy around her neck like he owned her, and she loved being owned. It was gross. She rested, inebriated and victorious. My helpless unraveling amused her; she was proud of herself. He pointed at me, "She's crying! Look at her," he laughed. "She's crying!"

They celebrated.

The sun was out but that living room was dark. Evil emanated from the loveseat and clouded the air. I stood in front of them; my open heart spilled a beautiful love across the floor. I had so much love to give and I wanted, with all of me, to give it to them but there was no fucking way. They wouldn't let me. I wouldn't let myself.

Clenching my teeth in angry tears, I jerked the Budweiser from her hands and gave the room one last good look. I knew I was searching for something I wouldn't find. I knew it was goodbye, so I paused in defeat and glared at them as they both grinned at me. Pissed off and broken, I wanted to break something so I bombed the bottle at my dad's head *so* fucking hard. He was the master manipulator behind it all and I wanted to crush his face. But I missed and dented the wall. Glass bust when it hit the tile floor and I left them with that—shattered.

* * *

That's how these drunk fucks are when they're onna bender though. They holler "Geronimo!" an jump off the wagon ho. They'll only *pretend* to catch themself by grabbin onta barstool, or the next fat Indian over. Otherwise they fall flat on their face hopin someone jus as desperate picks them up cripes. Pretty soon they're out there on The Log together, sittin in fronna Jimtown with mucka eyes. Throwin em back, they party pure hard til mornin. Sivuvanuts. Just sloppy an slobberin, they spit sweet nothings at each other or strut around actin cute. Hehzjeah, real cute too.

He'll tip his chin up quick an go, "Did'chyou know I always liked'chyou? We'd be ishpiv together. Man forreal, I always wun'ned you t'be my woman."

"Nay quit actin prairie then, shy guy. Get over here an gimme a kiss."

He'll lean in to'er an whisper, "I don't got no horses baby, but I can tie you up with rawhide real good, drag you back to my camp an give you some *meat*."

"Err-r-r-r-e-t!" she'll say pushin'em away, but really she wants to pull'em closer.

They'll sit on each'chother's laps an jus *laugh* like they're in love. There's no stars in their bloodshot eyes though, no butterflies flutterin either. The only thing in their belly is raunchy beer bubbles an BV. They'll burp an make out an hold dirty hands. Even onna crazy night like this there's no "getting to know each other" stage, because we're all from the rez an we've *always* all known each other! Strangers are jus cuzzints you haven't metch'yet. Shit even yer fresh snag is justa brand new old one.

They'll '49, or jam the hell out to classic rock, or jungle music, or worse—the only non-Christian radio station on the whole rez—*country*. They'll round bottles of SoCo til they're babysittin an fightin over spiders. People'll fuckin do crazy shit to get every last drop too like burn the glass witha lighter, as if that'll magically make more alcohol drip from the sides ho. By the end'a the night, everyone'll pair off tryina snag. Leather hands'll sneak up under each other's shirts or down each other's pants to squeeze soggy skin. Okss. They jus wanna bump uglies inna middle a'the night, or sweat on each'chother inna middle a'the day. Ooo jus plum rank.

Erbz they'll jus hook up with whoever too. They don't care if they're married, if *you're* married, if they have kids, if you have kids, if you *feed* yer kids, if you leftch'yer kids, if you have a job, if you have a car. Shit they don't even care if you have *teeth*. As long as you have couple dollars for nother shot of tequila, yer aight—or hawkables. They'll pawn yer TV to keep goin, or yer auntie's TV, or yer grandma's TV, or cheez they'll break into yer neighbor's house to steal their TV ho fuck. That's how these drunk fucks are when they're onna binge though. Wuh plum wicket.

Anythin t'getta Jimtown tho yut, shittiest place on earth. It's on the map too! An I don't jus mean the *social* map, like if you were powwow trailin through the Cheyenne Rez onna Fourtha July you'd know where I'm talkin bout. Anybody who's anybody who partied in Lame Deer knows Jimtown. No, I mean it's like actually a fucking *town* listed onna map. It's not even like Scenic in South Dakota that was once a town then died out an became a ghost town. No, the only thing that was ever here was this plum rugged ol shithole an its cruddy mountain of beer cans. I shit'chyou not there usta be this *wick* ol pile'a beer cans out back that stood taller'n the bar itself! It sat an sparkled in the daytime like a fucked up alcoholic Christmas tree ho. Recycled now but that's what made Jimtown famous, those cans.

The old owner, this guy named Bob Edwards said when asked about *when* that pile of cans started he said, "The pile of cans began the day Prohibition ended." Shew! I thought that was pretty funny. There's a jukebox in there but no barstools. The bar rail is nailed t'about fifteen cottonwood tree trunks each standin about a foot an a half tall. Ya know how many flat Indian asses in jeans hadda sit an smooth out those tree trunks? Jay-y-y-zah!

"I couldn't keep stools. They kept busting them over each other's heads." Hasivah! We must pure savage out! "Try picking up one of those trunks," he said. Holay. That Bob Edwards musta been a funny fucker. Course I never met em, I just found those quotes onna Internet inna *Kentucky New Era* article from 1977, same year my mom graduated high school.

***

My parents are dysfunctional codependents, typically connected at the hip. In all my life, I've rarely seen one without the other. The first time he came home drunk without her, they had gotten into an argument at the bar in Colstrip. This off-reservation border town is populated by country cowboys and coal miners who don't particularly *like* Indians, especially Indians who have had a few. Luckily my aunt was living there back then so my mom had somewhere to go. She walked across town intoxicated and got a ride back to the rez.

Us kids were home alone when Dad walked in with Auntie, Uncle, and another woman. She had a big nose, frizzy hair, and pop-bottle glasses. I didn't know who she was but she sat in my mom's spot. I asked Dad where Mom was and he so nonchalantly said, "I left her down there." I absolutely freaked. I hoped she was okay. I hid my brothers and sisters in the bedroom and kept them busy playing games. Every so often, I would venture down the hallway to check on the adults.

CCR was blasting at max on the surround sound. I came around the corner and caught them kissing on the couch. With instant rage, I slapped my dad straight in the face. It was the first time I cursed. I didn't really, though. All I said when I hit him was, "Dad, what the *hell* are you doing?" I screamed it, and the word scared me when it came out of my mouth. Before I could see how he received it, I scurried back to the bedroom.

I was twelve; I knew the situation was bad. I didn't know where my mom was. I didn't know when she was coming home—if she was *ever* coming home—and I didn't know how long the party in the living room would last. So I took charge and, one by one, lifted my three younger siblings up and out the window. I bent in half out over the sill, holding each child's hands as they used their feet to repel down the wall in front of the house. We all tried our best to avoid scrapes and bruises because those windows hurt. Deathly afraid of the adults exiting the front door and catching us, I moved my babies quickly. I couldn't have them see what I just saw. I had to save them, protect them. We had to go.

Once we were all out of the house, I threw the littlest on my hip and we ran up the dirt driveway. Crossing the cattleguard then the highway, we fled down the ditch and up again through the field to Grandma's house. I was so rattled. I told her everything I saw and she listened with an offensive calm. My entire life was falling apart: I was frantic, out of breath, and in tears. But Grandma just looked at me and nodded, then fed us and put on cartoons.

I figured she was afraid to call the cops on my dad. Everyone was. She stood in her living room peeking through the curtains to watch the house. She'd probably been doing that already anyway, noting which cars had come and gone. Everyone knows what everyone drives in our little town. Sometimes you can even recognize who's coming by the sound of their vehicle before you can even see it.

Soon after, Mom arrived back to the house and caught him too. From across the highway, we watched the explosion: uncoordinated bodies running around cars in the driveway, two units of tribal cops pulling in, Mom peeling out. She drove right across to retrieve us from Grandma's, which meant Dad and the others had probably watched us run away. They most likely thought, "Good, just let them go. Now we don't have to worry about them."

Mom packed her broken family into her sister's car and we made our way to the women's shelter in Billings. The only problem was that my older brother was at a friend's house and he missed the whole thing. We left him behind. The shelter was an oddly sterile place staffed with overly friendly white ladies. They were gross fake and made us do chores. Mom sat in the bedroom and cried a lot but I made friends with the other kids in the playroom. A baby twin drew me a picture and I kept it.

A short time later, it was one pathetically sober crying phone call from Dad and my mom's concern for her missing beating heart that brought us back. I was wary and untrusting the day Dad arrived to collect us. Knowing he was on his way to take us back to that house made something churn in my stomach.

The air was crisp against my face, that day. Frost crunched beneath my feet as I approached the car, reluctant to get in. Before we even stepped into the deceptive sunlight that morning, I'd placed my hands gently aside her cheeks and begged into her eyes. "Mom. Mom, *promise* me! Don't let him do this again, Mom. Promise me that the *next time* he hits you we're leaving again. Even once, Mom, promise?" She nodded, but I knew I was her backbone. Her own was broken.

* * *

Jimtown, man. I fuckin hate that place. The pissy sign bove the bar is shot up with a hunnerd bullet holes. Somehow they all missed. It says Jimtown *Saloon* but no one ever says that. Everybody calls it Jimtown Bar, Jimtown, or JT. Ol timers an hardcore locals call it Bunut. Jay yut boy Bunut, the Cheyenne word for downstream but everyone says down the road.

We gotta dry rez, so that sneaky fucker sits *just* off the rezline five miles northa town. Ee-e-e-ze we have bars jus off the rez in every direction actually! We got Kirby Saloon, Otter Creek Saloon, Office Bar an jayzah Club Buffet. Ashcan goes hard so Rabbit Town stays hoppin, all up and down the Mighty Tongue.

All these no good white guys been leechin off the reservation ever since reservations existed. Plum makin a *killin* off twitchin livers too, suckin the got'damn life outta our lil rez towns, ho outta our *moms and dads*. Fuck. They sell overpriced plastic bottles of Lewis and Clark vodka to thirsty Indians. Ho ignert enit, two lost ass white guys stumbled upon some Indians, now Indians stumble upon them an stumble even more. Sivah.

The worst part bout Jimtown is The Log! Well not the log itself but the *view* from The Log. There's not jus one log but bout four or five fifteen-foot logs, prolly the resta those cottonwood trees now that I think bout it. They lay out front like benches I s'pose. Sometimes you drive by the mornin after an jus see a couple legs hangin over cuz someone's pure assed out holay.

It's kinda like *a thing* ya know to sit on The Log. I swore I never would. But one time in high school, me an my goofy best fren were parked out front waitin for my parents who were inside takin their sweet ol time. We dared each other to get outta the car an go sit on The Log just for the hell of it. So we did. Dumb kids.

Get this, though. The view from The Log isn't really a bad view. It's beautiful actually. But it's *fucked* up! Right across the highway from Jimtown is the Deer Medicine Rocks. I always mess it up an call em the Medicine Deer Rocks but anyway, you should see how many cigarettes're up there hey.

Betch'you never even heard of em'uh? Well, lemme tellya. The Deer Medicine Rocks are the historical-ass sand rocks witha blue streak an the carvings, that the Thunder Beings threw lightning at. That's where muthafuckin Sitting Bull gave one hunnerd flesh offerings from all up an down his arms, chest, an back. Then he had his wakan vision of soldiers fallin upside down outta the sky.

That dream told em that we—the *Northern Cheyenne*, Lakota, an Arapaho—yes, in that order—were gonna murder Custer's pale ass, an his traitor Crow scouts, at the Battle of the Greasy Grass. Or you know, where we *reigned triumphant as victors of the Battle of the Little Big Horn having defeated the 7th Cavalry in the United States' greatest military defeat of all time.*

This was really only possible cuz us Cheyennes killed Crook's troops jus eight days before that at the Battle Where the Girl Saved Her Brother, or the Battle a'the Rosebud. Buffalo Calf Road Woman was the one who saved'er brother Chief Comes In Sight's ass, otherwise he wudda been purely waxed out an we wouldnt've won. Aye jokes, we still wudda won. But forreal, it was this same Cheyenne woman who clubbed Custer off his pissy pony justa couple days later, Buffalo Calf Road Woman.

I killed Custer because Custer was killed by Cheyenne women. Our women are warrior enough, our men din't even needa touch em. We shoved sticks into his head through his ears because they didn't work anyway. He didn't listen. We chopped his fingers off because he held the pipe but din't do it inna good way. We cut his tongue out for lyin when he spoke to us. He was forked-tongued like all th'other white guys. We cut his eyes out so he couldn't see on his journey to the other side. Shit for all I know he got lost an is still wanderin around Crow Agency!

A lotta people don't know the truth.

The Sioux got the glory, the Crow got the land, but the Cheyenne did the fighting. All those white headstones up onna battlefield an only four mark where Indians died. They're made outta red pipestone and they were jus barely even put up. They honor the Cheyenne suicide warriors who rode out first; one was my grandpa.

See, we can rattle these stories off because we grew up with these sacred sites all around us. We're reminded every got'damn day of our histories because we still live on the land where everything happened. Crusin downa dirt road with yer fam an someone'll point at somethin, "Right there is where…" then go off on some long ol story, simple as that. Even when yer by yourself, you see a rock or a ridge an some wicked ol scene plays out in yer head. Swear. Always dreamin bout the olden days…

But my point is: Who the *fuck* builds a bar so that the Deer Medicine Rocks are basically in yer fuckin parkin lot? No respect I swear to gawd. Cheyennes sit on The Log an watch the sun set behind those rocks now. They tell the stories an laugh an cry an warhoop an lulu an just drink an drink until they lose their got'damn minds, until *they're* the ones fallin upside down outta the sky. Pathetic man. I despise that place. Jimtown ruined my life.

And don't even *fuckin* get me started on Dead Man's Curve either. It's the first turn after you leave the bar an cross the rezline headin back towards town, deep ol ditches too. Everyone drunk from Jimtown has to pass Dead Man's Curve to get home. Highway planners designed a easy way to kill us off ho. My sister totaled her car on that turn. Luckily, she didn't die. We've lost *greats* on that turn. And their moms. We've lost our heroes, hopefuls, relatives, and nobodies on that turn.

JT is only four miles from my house so you can imagine how many people come knockin on our door askin for a ride down. Some jus plum pull in on their way back t'town. We see cop chases an people gettin pulled over all the time. Sometimes they set up that checkpoint right there by the Housing Authority, past Grandma's turnoff. You getta know who's partyin an how hard they're goin at it by watchin the cars go down. There's always that one or two that goes by just hootin an hollerin, honkin as they pass.

Fuh this one time I was sleep on the couch inna middle a'the night an our front door don't fit the frame good right? So in walks this guy, ripped out, pure tryina take his shirt off an get naked err. Dad musta heard'em fiddlin with the door cuz he came down the hallway right as this dude stumbled inna the TV. Dad shooed him away like a dog, "Shhht! Go on! Get outta here!" an pushed him out the front door. I was scared shitless!

I dunno why but that kinda reminds me of the time Uncle was partyin at our house. This was before he was tribal president, or maybe it was after. I can't member, but anyway he was all passin out onna couch an *errret* he jus straight started pissin on himself, right then an there! Dad kicked him out quick, halfway pushed an halfway dragged his ass to the door. We were kids playin outside then an all I remember is Dad slammin the door leavin Uncle leanin over the iron rail sideways, head in the chokecherry tree, hair all crazy, glasses half off, standin there onna concrete porch, pants on, all wet, halfway cryin, slobberin. He looked lost, blinkin his eyes slow, jus now woke up, an I felt bad for him like parta me wun'ned to help but his zipper was down an he was gross. Us kids screamed an ran round back a'the house. He never came around for a real long time after that. Actually, I dunno if he ever came back.

*   *   *

Sometimes they wouldn't come back. My parents would leave us saying, "We're going to make a quick run to Jimtown," but then disappear. Hours extended into days. I called Jimtown to check on them. The bartender would answer the phone and I'd ask if my parents were there. I can't believe it now, but she would actually let a child call and hand their parent the phone.

I'd scold my mom or dad, "When you coming home? Shhh, you said you were jus runnin right down and back! You better not be takin shots!" After that approach failed, I'd try pleading with them, "Well how much longer then? Man, just come home! You guys been gone all day. Did you even go to Colstrip an get us pizza like you said? We're hungry. Jus come home now, *please?*" Six. Four. Nine. Five. I've had that number memorized since childhood; it's one of few that's carved into my spine almost.

All day I would wait anxiously for my mom to come home: The one I would lay next to, whose beautiful black hair I'd play with. The one who had the softest skin in the world and the warmest hugs. The one who had the loveliest voice that was always ready to sing a song. I'd wait for my mom who had the AAAAAyyye-loud laugh, the one with beautiful boarding school penmanship. The one who would shake the tiny hands of babies she didn't even know, while waiting in line at the store. That sweet mom who smiled so hard her eyes would close. The one who would watch a movie with such an artistic eye, she'd recall the film in detail including the texture of the fabric a woman's dress was made from.

She had such a beautiful energy, the brightest smile, and the best words. Years later when I left for college across the country, she sent me on my way with a handwritten letter that read:

To my girl,

You take all my best. Share and be fulfilled. I go with you as you travel. Take the good and leave the bad. Hold your head up, shoulders back, and smile. Today is the day to live and love and laugh, and remember to be happy! I love you so much!

– MaMa

I saw girls on TV who were best friends with their moms, but my mom and her mother hardly spoke. I learned later it was because my mom felt my grandma abandoned her by sending her to boarding school at five years old. Gram thought she was doing what was right, giving her kids an "education," but Mom fell in line and became an institutionalized non-person like the rest of them. She grew up without a mother's love, no one to brush her hair or kiss her goodnight.

Instead, she was monitored by military-style dorm matrons who bullied orphan Indian kids. They learned to do what they were told without question or they'd get locked in a dark basement and left alone overnight. If they were beat or touched in a bad way, they had to keep their mouth shut. If they were caught running away, the punishment was much worse. Some girls chose self-harm and plotted a permanent escape.

Mom finally forgave Gram for sending her there, years later when she was an adult. I suppose they made up as best as they could after that. They'd talk here and there but it wasn't much. I would think of myself grown up and I didn't want things with my mother and me to be like they were with Mom and Gram. I wanted to be "best friends" like the white girls on TV. They always seemed to be talking about *boys* and dating. So in third grade I started telling my mom about every crush I ever had, even if it only lasted three days. That dumb boy talk forced Mom and I to grow close. Our relationship eventually grew into something beautiful and I missed her when she was gone.

I missed my dad, too. He was a big fella, not really tall but had a belly and a buzzcut. I'd fall asleep on his stomach sometimes. My dad was strong. When I was a little girl, I used to pretend I was sleeping when we'd return from long days spent in Billings just so he would carry me in the house. He'd tuck me in bed, whisper good night, and leave me with a kiss on the forehead. Dad had a great laugh, too. It was the kind that blasted out but ended silent, being just air and his belly jiggling. He was quick to laugh so hard he'd have to wipe his eyes. He had good teeth and they seemed to smile too when he laughed that hard.

Dad was an adventurer whose travels took our family on days-long road trips from the mountains of Montana to the desert in New Mexico to the sandy beaches of the Oregon coast, and back again. On the rez, Dad loved cruising the dirt roads through the hills and fishing. He showed me how to bait with corn, hook a work, and gut a fish. Leading by example, he silently taught me to appreciate the trees, love the sky, and hold onto the sunset as long as you can before you embrace the stars.

My dad was an intellectual. He studied philosophy and was one of the most educated people on the reservation. He made that clear to everyone on Northside when he got drunk, hollering out of the house, "I'm the smartest fucking Cheyenne *ever!* NO ONE is as smart as me! *No one!*" His capacity for conversation was one of the things I loved about him most. He'd make me think about things I've never thought about, like intersections of time.

"Every person is moving along their own timeline in life and for you to meet someone *at random* really isn't random at all, because as you're moving along this plane, they're moving along this plane," he'd say, talking with his hands, bringing them both together to create an X in front of his face. "And, at that very point, not only are you crossing physical paths but you have also met at an intersection of *time.* Everything that happened in your day, in your life, has led up to that moment where your time and the time of the event link up. Every car wreck, every friend you meet, *everything* is just reflecting an intersection of time. Think about that."

* * *

Chee we'd hafta do a lot of thinkin, make up alotta games to keep ourself busy. We'd have to entertain ourself for hours waitin for em. We'd play Kick-the-Can or Hide-and-Go-Seek or football until someone started cryin. Sivah my brother was jus *mean* too! He'd stand above you if you were hurt chun jus hollerin, "Poor sport! Poor sport!" Ooo I couldn't stand that. Neesh he was no good! Sometimes it pissed me off an made me jump up an keep playin. Other times I just laid there cryin, "*Shut up!* I'm gonna tell Mom and Dad on you!"

We had this huge ol yard an we were coo playin outside after dark, least til curfew. That siren went off at the police station bout a mile away but was still loud as shit. All the dogs on Northside would howl with that siren. It'd stop but they'd just keep howlin an howlin an howlin, just *cryin*. It was pissin scary! S'pose it happened every damn night an maybe I shudda got used to it but it always freaked me out. It felt like those cryin dogs were scared the spirits were comin out now an they was tellin us we better watch out an get inside. We'd take off inna the house afraid of Little People, Elbow Lady, or Goat Man. Holay jus scared of all kindsa gigis.

We'd be jus whinin around for Mom an Dad to come home but as soon as they'd get back err we'd pure wish they were gone again. We'd hear the car tires rattlin the cattleguard—*du-du-du-dun, du-du-du-dun* —and ho fuck we'd scream. "They're ho-o-o-o-o-me!" Piss all five of us would scatter, sometimes runnin right into each other sivuvanuts. We's halfway tryin to clean an halfway tryin to hide.

They'd come crashin through the door, usually Mom first tryina run from Dad. "I want a divorce!" he'd be hollerin. "Oh, *fuck you!*" she'd say or "Write it up, then! Print it out. I'll sign it." They'd stumble in loud, packin Budweiser an my dad's favorite, a bottle of Bacardi. Shit I learned howta be a bartender when I was old enough to pour his rum-to-Coke ratio. Or fuck before that when I was big enough to learn how to tip the glass an pour beer in so you don't make alotta foam.

They'd blast this one VHS recordin of a Mellencamp concert over an over an fuckin over again, as *loud* as the TV could go. It'd bout plum make us go deaf sivah. I'd cover both my ears, "Turn it do-o-o-o-w-wn!" Course they didn't. So we'd lock ourself inna back room. I tried to hide that tape once an all hell broke loose. Well like, worse than normal. Never did that again. John Cougar. Over an over an over again, I'm tellin you. Holy fuck I swear to GAWD if I ever hear Pink Houses or Paper In Fire one more time I'll kill somebody.

If we was lucky, Dad would sit onna couch jammin with his head back, eyes closed, whimperin around, tappin his one foot, cryin til he passed out. Mostly tho he'd be up big belly dancin in the livingroom. Chay all-out guy, spillin beer, spittin an singin at the top of his lungs as if his fat ass was on stage ho. Mom *loved* singin too. There were laughs an dances, until he'd flip his switch an punch her inna face. Party was over right then an'there. This is the part of drinkin I never could understand. Havin a loosy goosy good ol time then BAM! John fucking Cougar became the soundtrack to some fucked up shit, man. Can't even call it fightin cuz Dad's way bigger'n Mom and she never really did fight or talk back.

I's the big sister so I hadda take care a'the kids an keep em away from it. Sometimes they'd come bustin through the bedroom door, kickin our toys, ruinin our games, or jus straight steppin on us. It was always Mom first, Dad right behind her. Sweaty, bloody, smellin like stale beer, sometimes puke, sometimes naked.

Mom tried'a use us as a shield. She'd come in, dive onna bed, an surround herself with'er babies, hopin he'd chill out. He didn't. He'd jus stand above all of us, hollerin with full force, spit sprayin on us. He yelled so loud chee it made our ears ring. Our bodies got stiff. Every muscle froze. Our eyes stuck on him. It was like we couldn't breathe. He'd yell. She'd scream. We'd get thrown to the side. He'd attack. We'd holler, "Dad, *stop!*" Mom would look at me pure helpless. Our eyes would hold each other for one long second, then *pound pound pound,* the sound of belligerent fists hittin beautiful flesh.

"Go, go, go!" I'd tell my siblings t'run. I played musical bedrooms with my babies. I tried to keep'em from *seeing* it an we all pretended we couldn't hear it. Sometimes we played outside til the middle'a the night when we couldn't hear'em in there no more. We'd send one as a spy to peek through the window an make sure they were passed out fore we went back in. Mostly though, we did our best to stay hidden in a room away from where they were at. It'd get late an we still had skoo the next day. I'd sing my brothers an sisters to sleep over the sounds of fighting. Then I'd go check on Mom before fallin asleep, cryin, holdin onna my teddy bear for dear life.

Christ I'd see her all kindsa torn up.

Shitch'you never knew what the fuck you were gonna see when you came round that corner inna livingroom. It could be him straddlin her, two fists straight wailin on'er. She'd have both arms up in an X tryina protect herself cryin, "Stop! That's enough now-w-w! Navetnashiff!"

It could be her sittin onna couch, one leg up inna air tryina kick him away as he stood above her screamin, "Fuck you, ya fuckin bitch!" He'd lift his fist quick an pretend to swing just to watch'er whole body flinch. Ho he'd laugh.

It could be them side by side, her in a chokehold, no way to escape. "Do you love me? Tell me you fuckin love me!" he'd demand, then fuckin blast'er in the nose. Blood everywhere.

"I *love* you! You know I love you! WE ALL LOVE YOU! WE *ALL* LOVE YOU!" She'd spit red. He'd blast'er again.

It could be his whole body on toppa her whole body, smashin the *shit* outta her. She could be layin sideways with'er arm twisted all funny under em but he din't fuckin care. He'd hit'er head so hard it'd bounce off the floor. We'd hear her strugglin to *breathe* under em, worried she was gonna die right in fronna us. Her glasses were mostly always lost or broken and'er beautiful black hair was always all everywhere.

Sometimes he'd fuckin drag'er downa hallway by it. Her body'd slide down that white tile floor an'er screams would fill the whole house ho. Ho sometimes right after that, she'd jus go inna bathroom pure drunk an cryin an grab scissors an take em straight to'er head. Man, it'd tear me up to watch'er cut'er hair off like that. In tears, big lips, swollen face, nose runnin, black eye, she'd just go at it, throwin the cut off hair inna toilet.

I stood inna bathroom an begged'er to stop once. Tuggin at'er arm, I cried as I watched'er. "Mom, don't cut it! Mom, please don't cut it! *Please*, Mom. *Mo-o-om!*" She looked at me but she din't look at me. Then she jus handed me a broken heart handful of hair. I never tried'a stop'er ever again.

* * *

"Get the fuck outta my house, ya slut! Hit the highway! Go on, get the fuck outta here!" He'd say that but when she made her way to the door, he'd drag her backwards and throw her in the opposite direction. She chose to endure the beatings more often than not because she knew what would happen if she ran away. She stayed with him because of us. I know it.

Dad called her a BIA brat because she was raised in the government boarding school, not the Catholic one across the rez. She had a roof over her heard and dinner every night, even if it was only pickled beets or stewed tomatoes with bread in it. He, on the other hand, had a hungry, unstable childhood with two-timing, alcoholic parents. But she didn't have any—parents.

They were jealous of each other.

No matter how bad it got, she'd never *really* leave him. "I want my kids to have a mom and a dad," she'd cry. We'd heard it a million times. There were nights she'd break loose—I think only when she was afraid he'd really hurt her. *Hurt her* here meaning maybe *kill her*. Wherever I was in the house, I'd keep a keen ear to the sound of the windowpanes subtly ratting in their metal frames. This was the telltale sign that the front door had been opened and closed—she'd escaped.

That was my cue.

Adrenalin would pound throughout my little body. I'd run to the nearest east-facing window and search for her slow silhouette along the dark horizon. When I saw for sure which direction she went, I would scramble: Find her shoes. Find her jacket. Put on my shoes. My jacket. Grab my teddy. Tell the girls I love them. Then, jump out the window.

I could never let her go alone and there was no way I was staying in that house with him. I'd sprint as fast as I could to the far side of the yard. When I was younger, I would slither head first under the barbed wire fence, being sure not to catch my clothes or tear a hole in them when I did. When I got older, I learned to climb quickly to the top and jump over. Landing heavily on my hands and feet made me lose my breath for a second. I'd run hard and fast until I was hand-in-hand with the weeping woman, my beating heart.

I never knew where we were going. She never knew where we were going. We walked into the unknown together. She cried. I didn't. I was strong for her when she couldn't be strong for herself. I was fearless while deathly afraid. I didn't know what was head of us, but I knew what was behind us.

Stars witnessed our dark escape. The sound of freedom was gravel beneath our feet along a rural Montana highway. I told her, "Mom, breathe. Don't cry. We're alright now, Mom." She'd squeeze my hand, "I know." She tried to regain composure walking sloppy drunk. Her cries shot through the night sky before she'd inhale quickly and swallow them again.

She hated to leave her other children behind. I did too but I couldn't stay for them. Mom didn't have a job, money, a car or house of her own. He isolated her from her family and friends decades ago. I had to make sure that if she felt she had nothing in this entire *world*, she at least had me by her side. I walked tall. I walked steady. I carried my teddy bear in one hand. In the other, I carried my heart.

* * *

That was me an Mom though. I's the only one really there for'er an she's the only one really there for me. Nothin changed when I left for college either cept we hadda talk onna phone. I called'er plum pissin almos cryin over my first painting assignment once. *Paint an object important to you.* I didn't have much, nothin worth anythin. The only important thing I had all those years later was my teddy bear, a pink Pooh. Second t'Mom, My Baby was my only other ride-or-die. I couldn't travel 'thout him, sleep 'thout him, survive 'thout him—much less paint em for shit.

I called'er up, "Mom, I dunno how to do this! I jus wanna quit. I'd rather go read an write err at least I know how to do that!" She had good medicine for me though, "You're not supposed to know how to paint, my girl. That's why you're there, to *learn.* Just try. Take your time. I'll love it either way." No matter, I had'er back an she had mine.

Wuh when I'd come home on break though chee it was jus the same ol fucking sad song'n dance. Actually, I think they drank much more worser when I was home. They knew I'd hold down the fort while they were out gettin buck. Err I swear to gawd, drinkin an fightin like there was no tomorrow piss. I'd come home stressed as fuck straight off'a finals an dive back into rez life hard core. No let up. Two weeks later, it'd be time to turn around an start a brand new term. Cripes, *rugged* push an pull goin back an forth like that—pure vicious whiplash for me.

One time at the end'a break I was gettin ready to head'a Billints to catch my flight. I had jus a few hours to get there, an I's already on ndn time. My sisters were gonna cruise me up on my pony an keep my car (even though they din't have a license). I was packin inna back room. Outta nowhere my sister runs in an, "Mom just took off with your car!"

What? The fuck?

I ranna the fronna the house an sure'nough, empty driveway. Dad was assed out onna couch with his eyes closed so I knew she wun't go far. If they both bounced, I'd be screwed but Dad was still here so I knew she'd be back. I jus kept on packin, stackin my bags onna chair by the door—my teddy bear on top.

I decided I should prolly try to eat before the trip. Dad woke up at the smell of food an started bitchin so I fed em too. Mom was still gone on our only set'a wheels—*mine*. Right when he came to enough t'realize she left him, I really started to freak out bout not havin'nough time to make it to the airport. Ho then in she walks, hollerin like Dad, blood veins bulging.

"You aint goin *nowhere!* This is *our car* now!"

I stuck my hand out pure miserable, "Mom. Give me my keys."

She brushed past me, tryina throw elbows. Hehzjeah. I dunno what got her panties inna bunch, towards me no less. Before she got too far, I grabbed'er wrist with one hand an tried for the keys with the other. She jerked an twisted real quick. Fuck my hand started stingin *bad*. I thought a key sliced my left palm open. I squeezed'er wrist tighter tryina get control but holdin'er mean like that hurt *me*.

Sivah! She never did act like that towards me an I never did put my hands on'er. It felt gross right quick so I let'er go. She tried'a stagger straight, down the dark hallway. Sneakin behind her, I tried t'grab the keys as soon as she turned on the bathroom light. But I missed. Then she goes an throws my keys into the shitty, *unflushed* fuckin toilet—then flushes!

Fuck I froze for a second starin at the grodie gurgling water an swirling asswipe. I saw the end of my horsehair keychain stickin up an jus then, Mom pulled'er pants down to literally take a fuckin piss on my keys. My fucking keys! Before she could sit I pushed'er towards the bathtub, stuck my hand in, grabbed my keys, an threw em in the sink screamin.

"That's the *sickest fucking thing* I've ever seen in my entire fucking life! What the *FUCK*, Mom?"

My sister heard me flip. I was elbow deep in soap by the time she ran to the bathroom. Mom found'er way up outta the tub an back into her pants. I told my sister, "Go get everyone in the car. Let's get the fuck outta here!" Dad was makin noise, wonderin what was goin on. Mom left me inna bathroom. I scrubbed every knuckle, under every fingernail three times over yuck. Mom tol Dad what she did an I heard them laughin inna front room. Sick fucks.

I was sad I'd hafta go back to skoo without seein my mom an dad sober again, but that shit jus pissed me off so hard I jus wun'ned a'leave! My sisters were waitin for me inna car. I grabbed my bags from the couch. On my way to the door, Mom goes, all loud, "Well your baby won't miss you when you're gone! Your baby won't cry for you!" My head spun. My *baby?* My Baby!

"Mom, where's my teddy bear?"

"I flushed him down the toilet."

"Mom."

"I threw him in the trash."

"Mom!"

"Nope. Goodbye!"

"*Mom!*"

She fuckin switched teams! Got'dammit. Sometimes she'd do shit like this when she knew it was gonna be a long night with Dad, to maybe distract'em from bein on'er case or I don't fuckin know but she never did this to *me!* She was def puttin on a show for'em. She wouldn't tell me where he was. I tried'a picture myself onna plane without him an I started cryin. I couldn't go back without him. I couldn't *sleep* without em! She knew that! I was so fuckin ticked already, then she hit me right where she knew it'd hurt. Dad's shitty eyes lit up. Mom's silence tortured me.

They jus sat there enter*fucking*tained. Dad egged'er on by makin funna me. "Look at'er! She's a grown woman, cryin over a teddy bear! A fuckin *teddy bear!*" He laughed. I was onna mission. I looked inna bathroom, inna trash, behind the couches, under the kitchen table, on the fridge, *in* the fridge, in the freezer, oven, microwave, cupboards, cabinets, closets, washer, dryer, in anything that opened, under every chair, under every bed, even under *her* ho fuck. I looked everywhere!

I asked again where he was an she jus smiled this pissy smirk an pointed up. Like straight up. So what do I do? I went outside an walked all the way round the house, makin sure he wasn't onna roof. He wasn't onna roof. He wasn't outside.

Ooo she was jus tickled an Dad ate that shit up. For once he din't hafta do the work. She was doin it for'em. Every time I walked through the livingroom, "Mo-o-o-o-mmm, where is it?" She'd jus sit there. Not lookin at me. Not talkina me. Ew Dad loved it. Mom never fucked with me like this before. *Ever.*

"*Where* is he?" I hollered, panickin way wicked worse now cause time was runnin out. Still, she jus sat there, evil lookin at me. Dad kept laughin an laughin. *Ooofuck* I lost it! I walked up to'er an pulled'er fuckin glasses off'er face.

"You're not getting *these* back until I get him, then!"

No faze. She jus took a swig of beer an said, "Oh well. I can get another pair." Smug bitch. I hated that little look she had. Fuck I gave up. I felt terrible treatin my mom like that. She was twistin me inside out an I din't even know why.

This was my *mom*, man. My mom! We were a team. What did I do? What did I fucking do wrong? Why was she doing this? I didn't get it. Hatred turned to heartbreak. I went up to'er an grabbed'er by her chin. I turned'er head an made her look at me, made her look at my tears. I cried into'er eyes. I tried to find her.

"Where *is it*? Why are you *doing this* to me, Mom? Mom, *why?*"

* * *

I didn't know the woman on the couch with Dad, but she was ugly. She crossed her legs as easily as she'd just crossed me, and he loved her for it. He loved this woman, more than he loved my mom. In a mere twenty minutes, she had walked into our home and completely wrecked me. She then simply sat back liquor loose and leaned into him comfortably, as if she had spent thirty fucking years next to him. It was disgusting.

I never saw her before that day. He'd left my mother at Bunut and brought this bitch home. I hated her. I hated both of them and the psychotic smirks they wore. He was proud of her. He draped his arm heavy around her neck like he owned her, and she loved being owned. It was gross. She rested, inebriated and victorious. My helpless unraveling amused her; she was proud of herself. He pointed at me, "She's crying! Look at her," he laughed. "She's crying!"

They celebrated.

The sun was out but that living room was dark. Evil emanated from the loveseat and clouded the air. I stood in front of them; my open heart spilled a beautiful love across the floor. I had so much love to give and I wanted, with all of me, to give it to them but there was no fucking way. They wouldn't let me. I wouldn't let myself.

Clenching my teeth in angry tears, I jerked the Budweiser from her hands and gave the room one last good look. I knew I was searching for something I wouldn't find. I knew it was goodbye, so I paused in defeat and glared at them as they both grinned at me. Pissed off and broken, I wanted to break something so I bombed the bottle at my dad's head *so* fucking hard. He was the master manipulator behind it all and I wanted to crush his face. But I missed and dented the wall. Glass bust when it hit the tile floor and I left them with that—shattered.

The End

About the authors

Kenneth Dyer-Redner was born in Reno, Nevada and grew up on the Paiute-Shoshone Indian Reservation in Fallon, Nevada. After graduating from high school he moved to Texas and then Germany before returning to the reservation. During that two year span he began to read and write because, "Life just didn't seem to make sense." He then attended the University of Nevada, Reno where he fought for the historic Nevada Boxing Club and eventually received a degree in English in 2009. After college he moved to Phoenix, Arizona with his girlfriend and daughter. Throughout his life he's held various jobs which include: fast food worker, furniture delivery, youth center assistant, office supply delivery, fruit picker, warehouse associate, construction laborer, busboy, valet attendant, and recreation coordinator. He resides in Phoenix, Arizona with his wife, daughter, and son. Currently he is pursuing a Master's degree in American Indian Studies at Arizona State University. He writes fiction.

Adrian L. Jawort, Northern Cheyenne, has written freelance journalism and op-ed articles for some 13 very odd years at various national and indie publications. The curator of the *Off the Path* anthologies, he also has a dark fantasy novel under his belt, *Moonrise Falling*. Renown as a fearless and bold writer in both his non-fiction and fiction works, Jawort says, "You cannot create your own writing voice by continually drowning it out with the voices of what others may or may not think." He has a beautiful young daughter, Aurelia, who is very proud that people read her Daddy's written words.

Dana Lone Hill, Oglala Lakota (Sioux), was born and raised on the Pine Ridge Reservation in South Dakota. Dana started writing at the age of 4 and was published for her poetry at the age of 8. She is the mother of 4 children: Ty, Jalen, Stephon, and Justice. She is a freelance writer for *The Guardian, Lakota Country Times, The Intersection of Madness and Reality,* and *LA Progressive.* Dana is also the author of the popular "rez sensation" fiction novel, *Pointing With Lips, A Week In the Life of a Rez Chick,* and the follow up novel *Pointing With Lips Volume II* is due out in 2015. She enjoys beading, quilling, painting,writing, watching the New York Yankees, and chick flicks. Dana believes that despite hardships, they can be turned into good things if you look at them in the right light at the right angle. She would not change one step she ever took on this beautiful planet because every one of those steps made her into who she is. She has a blog at www.justarezchick.wordpress.com.

Bojan Louis is a member of the Navajo Nation — Naakai Dine'é; Ashiihí; Ta'neezahnii; Bilgáana. His poems have appeared or are forthcoming in *The Kenyon Review, Platte Valley Review, Hinchas de Poesía, American Indian Research and Culture Journal,* and *Black Renaissance Noire*; his fiction in *Alaska Quarterly Review* and *Yellow Medicine Review*; his creative nonfiction in *As/Us Journal*. He is the author of the nonfiction chapbook, *Troubleshooting Silence in Arizona* (Guillotine Series, 2012). He has been a resident at The MacDowell Colony. He earns his ends and writing time by working as an electrician, construction worker, and full-time English Instructor at Arizona State University's Downtown Campus.

Sterling HolyWhiteMountain grew up on the Blackfeet Reservation, where he lived the first part of his life according to the laws of the old time basketball religion. He has received a BA in English Creative Writing from the University of Montana, an MFA in Fiction from the Iowa Writers' Workshop, and was a James C. McCreight Fiction Fellow at the University of Wisconsin. He currently directs the writing center at Blackfeet Community College, and is working on a collection of novellas. He is an unrecognized citizen of the Blackfeet Nation.

Kristiana Kahakauwila's first book, *This is Paradise: Stories*, is set in contemporary Hawai`i and explores ideas of Nativeness and nativity. Selected for the Barnes and Noble's Discover Great New Writers program, *This is Paradise* received praise from the *New York Times*, *O, The Oprah Magazine*, and *Elle*, among others. Of kanaka maoli and German-Norwegian descent, Kristiana identifies as hapa. In Hawaiian, hapa literally means less than whole, and refers to race. But Kristiana's work is an attempt to reclaim that diminished space as something more-than—not just in terms of race but also ethnicity, culture, gender, sexuality, class, and ability. "Most of my stories begin with a question I'm trying to answer for myself," she says. "The story isn't an answer. It's my search for an answer." A graduate of University of Michigan's M.F.A. program, she teaches creative writing at Western Washington University in Bellingham, WA, and is an avid runner and surfer.

K.M. Harris: Woman. Maori. Writer – three simple words.
In New Zealand, the Maori people have a saying; 'iti te kupu, nui te koorero,' which in English, loosely means 'a few words can provide a greater explanation,' and aspiring Maori Writer K.M Harris exudes the meaning of each of these words in her own unique way. Representing New Zealand Maori in Off The Path Vol. 2, K.M Harris hails from the northern New Zealand tribe of Ngapuhi with connections to tribes in the Bay of Plenty and East Coast regions. She is the author of the non-fiction novel, *Eight Women: Pure Platinum People*. Real experiences from real people is the kind of writing K.M Harris enjoys producing and 'reality reads' is what she calls it. Writing to cater to an open minded audience by capatilising on stories from her own cultural history and short career in the New Zealand Army, is how K.M Harris has been able to kick-start her writing journey towards becoming a published author. K.M Harris loves being involved in Maori cultural activities with her family and friends, and enjoys keeping fit and healthy through meditative running, Bikram Yoga, swimming and listening to music.
www.maoriwriter.com

Ellen van Neerven is a young Yugambeh woman from South-East Queensland, Australia. She is the author of the award-winning *Heat and Light* (UQP, 2014). Divided into three sections, it is inspired by the intersection of familial history, location and identity. Ellen has been awarded a Queensland Writers Fellowship to pursue her next project in 2015, a novel about Aboriginal relationships with megafauna. She lives in Brisbane where she works as the senior editor of the *blackandwrite!* project at the State Library of Queensland. She is the editor of *Writing Black*, a new digital collection of Australian Indigenous writing, and enjoys soccer, tennis and dancing with other writers.

Bill Wetzel is Amskapi Pikuni aka Blackfeet from Montana. He's a former bull rider/wrestler turned writer/humorist. He is a coauthor of the short story collection *The Acorn Gathering*. His work has appeared in the American Indian Culture and Research Journal, Yellow Medicine Review, Studies In Indian Literatures (SAIL), Hinchas de Poesia, Red Ink Magazine, Literary Orphans and the *Best Of Literary Orphans: The Greater Secrets*. He is also the curator for the Stjukshon Indigenous reading series at Casa Libre en la Solana in Tucson, AZ. No bulls or bears were harmed in the writing of his short story.

Cinnamon Spear (Mo'kee'e) was raised in a large family on the Northern Cheyenne Reservation in Montana. Since before she could speak, her mother encouraged: Use your words. Now her words are a release, and her resistance. Writing is a freedom, but also her duty. She taught her pen to capture shadows and put darkness on paper so she could keep shining for the Morning Star People. Cinnamon is the only graduate of Lame Deer High School to attend the Ivy League, or graduate school. She earned a BA in Native American Studies from Dartmouth College in 2009. She returned to complete a Masters of Arts in Liberal Studies degree in 2013, concentrating on Creative Writing. Cinnamon regularly returns home to promote the arts and encourage the youth. She offers, "My work may be hard to read, because it is hard to write. It's not meant to hurt—it is meant to heal. These stories are not mine. They are ours. Let the healing begin."

Made in the USA
Lexington, KY
15 August 2017